DIGITAL TELEVISION: ON THE THRESHOLD

DIGITAL TELEVISION: ON THE THRESHOLD

MARK L. GOLDSTEIN
(EDITOR)

Novinka Books
New York

For permission to use material from this book please contact us:
Telephone 631-231-7269; Fax 631-231-8175
Web Site: http://www.novapublishers.com

NOTICE TO THE READER

The Publisher has taken reasonable care in the preparation of this book, but makes no expressed or implied warranty of any kind and assumes no responsibility for any errors or omissions. No liability is assumed for incidental or consequential damages in connection with or arising out of information contained in this book. The Publisher shall not be liable for any special, consequential, or exemplary damages resulting, in whole or in part, from the readers' use of, or reliance upon, this material.

This publication is designed to provide accurate and authoritative information with regard to the subject matter covered herein. It is sold with the clear understanding that the Publisher is not engaged in rendering legal or any other professional services. If legal or any other expert assistance is required, the services of a competent person should be sought. FROM A DECLARATION OF PARTICIPANTS JOINTLY ADOPTED BY A COMMITTEE OF THE AMERICAN BAR ASSOCIATION AND A COMMITTEE OF PUBLISHERS.

LIBRARY OF CONGRESS CATALOGING-IN-PUBLICATION DATA

Goldstein, Mark L.
  Digital television : on the threshold / Mark L. Goldstein.
    p. cm.
  ISBN 978-1-60456-693-2 (hardcover)
  1. Digital television. 2. Television--Receivers and reception. I. Title.
  TK6678.G65 2008
  384.55--dc22

                        2008015999

Published by Nova Science Publishers, Inc. ✛ New York

CONTENTS

PREFACE

On February 17, 2009, federal law requires all full-power television stations in the United States to cease analog broadcasting, enabling the government to reclaim valuable spectrum that the broadcasters currently use for analog broadcasts. This change, often referred to as the digital television (DTV) transition, requires action by broadcasters and consumers to ensure broadcast television signals are still available and viewable. The National Telecommunications and Information Administration (NTIA) created a program to subsidize consumers' purchases of digital-to-analog converter boxes. After the transition, households with analog sets that rely on over-the-air broadcast signals must take action or they will lose television service, but some households might not be aware of this potential disruption.

In: Digital Television: On the Threshold
Editor: Mark L. Goldstein, pp. 1-20

ISBN: 978-1-60456-693-2
© 2008 Nova Science Publishers, Inc.

Chapter 1

DIGITAL TELEVISION TRANSITION PRELIMINARY INFORMATION ON PROGRESS OF THE DTV TRANSITION[*]

Government Accountability Office

WHY GAO DID THIS STUDY

On February 17, 2009, federal law requires all full-power television stations in the United States to cease analog broadcasting, enabling the government to reclaim valuable spectrum that the broadcasters currently use for analog broadcasts. This change, often referred to as the digital television (DTV) transition, requires action by broadcasters and consumers to ensure broadcast television signals are still available and viewable. The National Telecommunications and Information Administration (NTIA) created a program to subsidize consumers' purchases of digital-to-analog converter boxes. This testimony provides preliminary information on (1) the progress made by federal entities, and others, to facilitate the transition, (2) the progress in the education of consumers about the transition, (3) the progress made in implementing the converter box subsidy program, (4) technical issues of the transition, and (5) future GAO work on the progress of the DTV transition. GAO interviewed officials with the Federal Communications Commission (FCC) and NTIA. Further, GAO interviewed a wide variety of industry and other stakeholders involved with the transition, including members of the DTV Transition Coalition—a group of public and private

---

[*] This chapter is an excerpted, indexed edition of GAO Report GAO-08-191T, Dated October 17, 2007

stakeholders, and experts on strategic communications. GAO discussed this testimony with FCC and NTIA officials and incorporated their comments.

WHAT GAO FOUND

FCC and NTIA, in conjunction with other stakeholders, have taken steps to facilitate the DTV transition. For example, FCC has conducted periodic reviews to report on transition progress, and NTIA has issued a contract for administering the converter box subsidy program. In addition, private sector industries have also begun preparing for the transition. Despite public-private sector interaction designed to help facilitate the transition, we found that no comprehensive plan exists for the DTV transition. Without such a plan, meaningful guidance for coordinating responsibilities and measuring progress might not be available to the private or public sector.

Several federal and private stakeholders have begun consumer education campaigns. FCC and NTIA have developed informational materials and begun direct outreach to consumer groups. In addition, private industry stakeholders created the DTV Transition Coalition and are voluntarily conducting outreach efforts. However, these efforts are in the planning stages and challenges remain. An expert panel that GAO convened identified potential challenges and key practices for a consumer education campaign.

NTIA has made progress in implementing the converter box subsidy program, but the program's outcome depends on the voluntary participation of retailers and manufacturers. Retailers we contacted expressed concerns about the possibility of a redemption system that would affect their point-of-sale systems and stated they would need more information on IBM's technical solution before they could assess the impact on their systems and whether it would affect their participation. With limited or delayed retailer participation, consumers might face difficulties in redeeming their coupons for eligible converter boxes.

Most television stations already transmit a digital signal, but technical and coordination issues, such as antenna replacement and tower construction, may present challenges for broadcasters. In addition, cable and satellite television providers must coordinate with broadcasters to ensure that they can continue to receive and transmit the digital broadcast signals. Further, certain stations that retransmit the television signals, known as translator stations, are not required to cease analog broadcasting. These stations may choose to retransmit a digital signal, or they may convert the digital signal to analog and continue to broadcast in analog after February 2009.

We plan on reporting on the progress of the DTV transition, including the status of consumer education and awareness about the DTV transition, IBM and NTIA's administration of the converter box subsidy program, and industry technical preparations throughout the upcoming transition period. We will continue to monitor government and industry consumer education efforts and plan to analyze the efforts compared with key practices for consumer outreach. In addition, we plan to survey broadcasters on the technical issues that must be addressed prior to the DTV transition date.

Mr. Chairman and Members of the Subcommittee:

I am pleased to be here today to report on our work on the progress made in the nation's transition to digital television (DTV). We have a detailed report on public and private sector efforts underway to implement the transition that will be issued in November 2007. The findings that I am reporting to the Subcommittee today are based on our draft report and are therefore preliminary.

A primary goal of the DTV transition is for the federal government to reclaim spectrum[1] that broadcasters currently use to provide analog television signals. The spectrum that the federal government will reclaim at the end of the transition is considered highly valuable because of its particular technical properties. In all, the DTV transition will free up 108 megahertz (MHz) of spectrum. The Federal Communications Commission (FCC) has reallocated 24 MHz of the spectrum that will be recovered for public safety purposes, which became a higher priority following the terrorist attacks of September 11, 2001. FCC will auction the remaining spectrum for commercial purposes, with the resulting proceeds allocated for, among other things, reducing the federal deficit.

The Digital Television Transition and Public Safety Act of 2005 mandates the cessation of analog television broadcast signals on February 17, 2009. After that date, households who view television on analog sets solely through the reception of over-the-air signals must take action to ensure that they have the necessary equipment, such as a digital-to-analog converter box, or subscription video service to be able to view the digital broadcast signals. If they do not take such action, they will lose the ability to view the digital signals on their analog sets; i.e., they will not be able to watch television programs. The act also directed the National Telecommunications and Information Administration (NTIA) to establish a $1.5 billion program through which households can obtain coupons for the purchase of digital-to-analog converter boxes. NTIA issued a final rule that adopted regulations to implement the converter box subsidy program, and in August 2007, selected IBM Corporation (IBM) to administer the program. Beginning January 1, 2008, households can request up to two $40 coupons toward the purchase of eligible[2] digital-to-analog converter boxes.

Although it is unclear what percentage of households who rely exclusively on over-the-air broadcasts have analog sets, potentially millions of those households stand to be left without any television service unless they take action. To help the public understand the DTV transition and the various options they have, consumer education and awareness programs are underway and additional programs are being planned.

My testimony today will focus on progress made in the DTV transition. In particular, I will discuss (1) the progress made by federal entities, in conjunction with other stakeholders, in facilitating the transition, (2) the progress made in educating consumers about the transition and any related challenges, (3) the progress made in implementing a subsidy program for converter boxes and any related challenges, (4) the technical issues facing the broadcast industry in meeting the transition, and (5) future work on the progress of the DTV transition that we will undertake.

To meet these objectives, we reviewed government documents and interviewed officials with FCC and NTIA, the steering committee members of the Digital Television Transition Coalition, as well as a wide variety of industry and other private stakeholders, such as broadcasters, satellite television providers, cable companies, manufacturers, retailers, industry associations, and consumer advocacy groups. Further, we consulted strategic communications experts representing public, private, and academic organizations to identify potential challenges that might obstruct consumer education efforts, as well as key practices for consumer outreach campaigns. We reviewed FCC and NTIA rules and proposed rule-makings related to the digital television transition, and the comments they received in response to the proposed rule-makings. Finally, we reviewed NTIA's request for proposals for administering the converter box subsidy program, and related contract documents. We performed our review from January 2007 through October 2007 in accordance with generally accepted government auditing standards. We discussed this testimony with FCC and NTIA officials to obtain their comments. FCC and NTIA provided additional information that we incorporated where appropriate.

IN SUMMARY

- FCC and NTIA, in conjunction with other stakeholders, have taken steps to facilitate the DTV transition. For example, FCC has conducted periodic reviews to report on transition progress, and NTIA has issued a contract for administering the converter box subsidy program. In addition, private sector industries have also begun preparing for the transition. Despite public-private sector interaction designed to help facilitate the transition, we found that no comprehensive plan exists for the DTV transition. Without such a plan, meaningful guidance for coordinating responsibilities and measuring progress might not be available to the private or public sector.
- Several federal and private stakeholders have begun consumer education campaigns, with both independent and coordinated efforts underway. FCC and NTIA have developed informational materials and begun direct outreach to consumer groups. In addition, private industry stakeholders created the DTV Transition Coalition and are voluntarily conducting outreach efforts. However, these efforts are in the planning stages, and challenges remain. An expert panel that we convened identified potential challenges and key practices for a consumer education campaign, such as defining goals and objectives and establishing metrics to measure success.

- NTIA has made progress in implementing the converter box subsidy program, but the program's outcome depends on the voluntary participation of retailers and manufacturers. Retailers we contacted expressed concerns about the possibility of a redemption system that would affect their point-of-sale systems and stated they would need more information on IBM's technical solution before they could assess the impact on their systems and whether it would affect their participation. With limited or delayed retailer participation, consumers might face difficulties in redeeming their coupons for eligible converter boxes.

- Although most television stations already transmit a digital signal, technical and coordination issues, such as antenna replacement and tower construction, may present challenges for broadcasters in preparing for the DTV transition. In addition, cable and satellite television providers must coordinate with broadcasters to ensure that they can continue to receive and transmit the digital broadcast signals after the transition. Further, select stations that retransmit television signals, known as translator stations, are not required to cease analog broadcasting. These stations may choose to retransmit a digital signal, or they may convert the digital signal to analog and continue to broadcast in analog after February 2009.

- We plan on reporting on the progress of the DTV transition, including public and private efforts in facilitating the transition, the status of consumer education and awareness about the DTV transition, IBM and NTIA's administration of the converter box subsidy program, and industry technical preparations throughout the upcoming transition period. For example, we will continue to monitor consumer education programs and plan to conduct a series of consumer surveys throughout the year prior to the transition date. The surveys we conduct will be aimed at determining the population that will be affected by the DTV transition and the public awareness of the transition. Throughout the transition process, we will continue to monitor government and industry consumer education efforts and analyze the efforts compared with key practices for consumer outreach. In addition, we plan to survey broadcasters on the technical issues that must be addressed prior to the DTV transition date.

BACKGROUND

The DTV transition will enable the government to allocate valuable spectrum from analog broadcast to public safety and other purposes. Further, digital transmission of television signals provides several advantages compared to analog transmission, such as enabling better quality picture and sound reception as well as using the radiofrequency spectrum more efficiently than analog transmission. With traditional analog technology, pictures and sounds are converted into "waveform" electrical signals for transmission through the radiofrequency spectrum, while digital technology converts these pictures and sounds into a stream of digits consisting of zeros and ones for transmission.

The Digital Television Transition and Public Safety Act of 2005 addresses the responsibilities of two federal agencies—FCC and NTIA—related to the DTV transition. The act directs FCC to require full-power television stations to cease analog broadcasting on February 17, 2009. While full-power television stations are required to terminate their analog signals, this deadline does not apply to translator television stations. Translator stations receive a signal from a television station and simultaneously retransmit the signal on another channel. These stations are intended to provide service to areas where direct reception of full-service broadcast stations is unsatisfactory because of distance or terrain obstructions, such as in mountainous regions.

As we have previously reported, households with analog televisions that rely solely on over-the-air television signals received through a rooftop antenna or indoor antenna must take action to be able to view digital broadcast signals after the termination of analog broadcasts. Options available to these households include (1) purchasing a digital television set that includes a tuner capable of receiving, processing, and displaying a digital signal; (2) purchasing a digital-to-analog converter box, which converts the digital broadcast signals to analog so they can be viewed on an existing analog set; or (3) subscribing to a cable, satellite, or other service to eliminate the need to acquire a digital-to-analog converter box. The act also directed NTIA to establish a $1.5 billion subsidy program through which households can obtain coupons toward the purchase of digital-to-analog converter boxes. The last day for consumers to request coupons is March 31, 2009, and coupons will be redeemed through July 9, 2009. As required by law, all coupons expire 90 days after issuance. Consumers can redeem their coupons at participating retailers (both "brick and mortar" and online) for eligible converter boxes.

To help inform consumers about the transition, in February 2007, eight private sector organizations launched the Digital Television Transition Coalition. These eight organizations are the Association for Maximum Service Television, Association of Public Television Stations, Consumer Electronics Association, Consumer Electronic Retailers Coalition, Leadership Conference on Civil Rights, LG Electronics, National Association of Broadcasters, and the National Cable and Telecommunications Association. These founding organizations comprise the Coalition's steering committee and make decisions on behalf of the Coalition. To better represent the interests of at risk or underserved populations—such as the elderly—AARP later joined the steering committee. The Coalition's mission is to ensure that no consumer is left without broadcast television due to a lack of information about the transition.

Currently, the Coalition has over 160 member organizations comprised of business, trade and industry groups, as well as FCC.[3]

Recent surveys conducted by industry trade associations indicate that consumer awareness of the digital transition is low. The Association for Public Television Stations reported in January 2007 that 61 percent of participants surveyed had "no idea" that the transition was taking place. Another study conducted by the National Association of Broadcasters focused on households that primarily receive their analog television signals over-the-air—and will therefore be most affected by the transition—and reported that 57 percent of those surveyed were not aware of the transition. Both surveys found that almost all people with some awareness of the transition had limited awareness of the date the transition will take place.

FEDERAL ENTITIES AND OTHER STAKEHOLDERS ARE FACILITATING THE TRANSITION, BUT COMPREHENSIVE PLANNING AND RISK MANAGEMENT IS LIMITED

FCC and NTIA, in conjunction with other stakeholders, have taken steps to facilitate the DTV transition. FCC has primary responsibility to regulate the television broadcast industry for the federal government and has taken a number of actions regarding the transition. For example, FCC has proposed and set deadlines to upgrade station equipment to send digital signals. In addition, FCC has conducted periodic reviews to report on transition progress and held a workshop for interested parties to discuss transition challenges and issues. NTIA has statutory responsibility for the converter box subsidy program, and it has issued a contract in preparation for that program's development. Private sector industries, including broadcasters, manufacturers, and retailers have also begun preparing for the transition. Despite public-private sector interaction designed to help facilitate the transition, we found that no comprehensive plan exists for the DTV transition. Among other things, a comprehensive plan can detail milestones and key goals, which provide meaningful guidance for assigning and coordinating responsibilities and deadlines and measuring progress. Such planning also includes assessing, managing, and mitigating risks, which can help organizations to identify potential problems before they occur and target limited resources. We have previously reported on the benefits of managing risks, including assisting other organizations involved in high stakes efforts similar to the DTV transition. For example, we credited one federal agency's success in weathering the potential for critical computer system failures during the Year 2000 Computer Conversion (Y2K), in part, due to reducing risks to facilities, systems, programs, and services during the critical rollover period.

PROGRESS IN CONSUMER EDUCATION ON THE DTV TRANSITION HAS BEEN MADE, BUT WIDESPREAD IMPLEMENTATION IS NOT YET UNDERWAY

FCC and NTIA, along with industry and other private stakeholders, have made progress in educating consumers about the DTV transition. For example, FCC and NTIA have developed informational materials on the transition and begun outreaching directly to consumer and stakeholder groups. Both agencies are also involved with the Digital Television Transition Coalition, a group representing over 160 business, trade, grass roots, and other organizations whose purpose is to provide consumers with information about the transition. Private industry stakeholders are voluntarily taking the lead on planning public service announcements, developing Web sites, and garnering media coverage on the transition. While federal and private stakeholders have taken these initial steps, the initiative is still largely in the planning stages and widespread efforts have yet to be implemented. Further, because of the number of public and private sector entities involved in consumer education efforts for the transition and the timing, coordination and content of the messages they produce, consumers might become confused over what steps, if any, are necessary to avoid disruptions to their television viewing after the transition date.

To identify the difficulties and challenges to consumer education and outreach, we convened an expert panel to discuss consumer education issues applicable to the DTV transition, including potential challenges that may obstruct efforts and the key planning components of a consumer education campaign that will help to overcome some of those challenges. Expert panel members as well as other private and public sector officials highlighted several challenges, as follows:

Prioritizing limited resources. With limited time and financial resources, it is likely to be a challenge for stakeholders to determine how best to allocate those resources within the campaign—for example, whether to target a smaller audience over a set period of time, versus targeting a broader audience over a shorter period of time.

Educating consumers who do not necessarily need to take action. Many of the outreach efforts will be focused on educating consumers on what to do to keep their television sets from going dark after the termination of analog broadcasts. However, a large proportion of U.S. households will not need to do anything—for example, because they have cable or satellite television service that will enable their analog set to continue to display programming. Because many messages focus on the actions that households that rely on over-the-air analog broadcasting need to take, consumers unaffected by the transition may become confused and purchase equipment they do not need. In our past work looking at a similar digital transition in Germany, we have described this potential confusion to cable and satellite households as a challenge of educating consumers about the transition.[4]

Reaching underserved populations. Conveying the message to underserved populations—for example, senior citizens, disabled, those residing in rural areas, or non-English speaking households will provide an added challenge. For example, many groups outreaching to consumers about the transition are doing so on Web sites, which may not be available to people who lack Internet access or are less technically savvy. Another challenge is providing information in a wide variety of formats, such as in different languages for non-English speaking consumers and in text, video, voice, and Braille for the disabled. Overall, a challenge of consumer education is that those households in need of taking action may be the least likely to be aware of the transition.

Aligning stakeholders. Panel members and other industry representatives also noted the challenge of aligning stakeholders—some who are natural competitors—to work together. In our past work, we have reported that federal agencies engaged in collaborative efforts—such as the transition—need to create the means to monitor and evaluate their efforts to enable them to identify areas for improvement. Reporting on these activities can help key decision makers within the agencies, as well as clients and stakeholders, to obtain feedback for improving both policy and operational effectiveness.[5]

In addition to highlighting potential challenges, the expert panelists identified the following key practices as important to planning a consumer education campaign that will motivate consumers to take the steps needed to avoid television viewing disruptions, as well as help to alleviate identified challenges along the way:

Table 1. Key Practices for Consumer Education Planning

Key Practice	Description
Define Goals and Objectives	Define the goals of the communications campaign, e.g., to increase awareness or motivate a change in behavior. Define the objectives that will help the campaign meet those goals.
Analyze the Situation	Analyze the situation, including any competing voices or messages, related market conditions, and key dates or timing constraints. Review relevant past experiences and examples to identify applicable "lessons learned" that may help to guide efforts.
Identify Stakeholders	Identify and engage all the key stakeholders who will be involved in communications efforts. Clarify the roles and responsibilities of each stakeholder, including which entity or entities will lead overall efforts.
Identify Resources	Identify available short- and long-term budgetary and other resources.

Table 1. Continued

Key Practice	Description
Research Target Audiences	Conduct audience research, such as dividing the audience into smaller groups of people who have relevant needs, preferences and characteristics, as well as measuring audience awareness, beliefs, competing behaviors, and motivators. Also, identify any potential audience-specific obstacles, such as access to information.
Develop Consistent, Clear Messages	Determine what messages to develop based on budget, goals, and audience research findings. Develop clear and consistent audience messages; test and refine them.
Identify Credible Messenger(s)	Identify who will be delivering the messages and ensure that the source is credible with audiences.
Design Media Mix	Plan the media mix to optimize earned media (such as news stories or opinion editorials) and paid media (such as broadcast, print, or Internet advertising). Identify through which methods (e.g., advertising in newsprint ads), how often (e.g., weekly or monthly) and over what duration (e.g., 1 year) messages will reach audiences.
Establish Metrics to Measure Success	Establish both process and outcome metrics to measure success in achieving objectives of the outreach campaign. Process metrics assure the quality, quantity, and timeliness of the contractor's work. Outcome metrics evaluate how well the campaign influenced the attitudes and behaviors of the target audience(s) that it set out to influence.

Source: GAO analysis of expert panel discussion

While still too early to evaluate the Coalition's consumer education efforts, the Coalition has employed strategies consistent with the key practices identified by the expert panel. For example, the Coalition has identified stakeholders and conducted focus groups to test and refine its consumer messages. However, at the time of our report, it remains unclear whether public-private sector interaction can ensure a consistent message to prevent confusion or unnecessary purchases on the part of consumers. Moreover, the absence of comprehensive planning to assess and mitigate risks associated with the transition, including outreach efforts, may increase the potential for at risk populations not adequately preparing for the transition.

NTIA HAS TAKEN STEPS TO IMPLEMENT A SUBSIDY PROGRAM FOR CONVERTER BOXES, BUT CHALLENGES REMAIN

NTIA has made progress in implementing the converter box subsidy program, including soliciting stakeholder comments, meeting with industry participants, and selecting IBM in August 2007 to administer the program. The subsidy program's outcomes depend on the coordination and participation of NTIA, IBM, converter box manufacturers, retailers, and consumers. Manufacturers and retailers are voluntarily participating in the program, as NTIA does not have the authority to require their participation. IBM will develop the technical solution for the program, which includes determining how consumers will request, receive, and redeem coupons, and how this will affect retailers' current point-of-sale systems.[6] NTIA and IBM will also be conducting consumer outreach specific to the program. Figure 1 depicts the necessary, interrelated actions for the subsidy program.

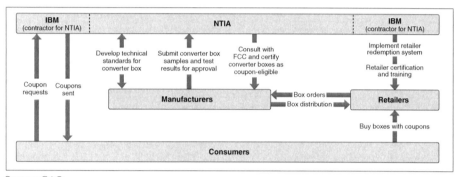

Source: GAO.

Figure 1. Coordination of Groups Involved in the Subsidy Program.

As shown in figure 2, consumers can begin applying for converter box coupons starting January 1, 2008, with NTIA requiring full distribution of coupons to begin by April 1, 2008. Consequently, some consumers that request coupons in January might have to wait months to receive their coupons. Complicating matters is uncertainty regarding retailer participation and readiness. At the time of our review, several retailers we contacted expressed concerns about the possibility of a redemption system that would affect their point-of-sale systems, noting that modifying these systems can be time-consuming, resource-intensive, and expensive, and can affect their other financial systems. Retailer representatives told us they will need more information about the contractor's technical solution before they could assess the impact on their systems and whether it would affect their participation. Further, they said that March or April of 2008—3 to 4 months after consumers can begin requesting coupons—is a more likely time frame for retailers to be ready to participate in the program. The extent to which point-of-sale system modifications will be necessary and the potential impact on retailers will remain unknown until IBM presents its technical solution. With limited or delayed retailer participation, consumers might face difficulties in redeeming their coupons for eligible converter boxes during the designated time period. Some manufacturer, advocacy, and retailer representatives we contacted expressed concern about consumers' ability to find participating retailers that are able to redeem coupons and have converter boxes in stock. The final rule does not require remedies if certain geographic areas lack participating retailers and NTIA does not have the explicit authority to require that participating retailers maintain a certain level of inventory. Thus, it is uncertain whether consumers with coupons will be able to locate a participating retailer with converter boxes in stock.

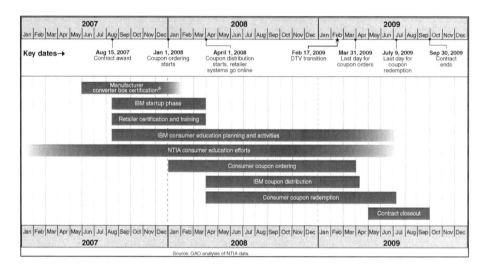

Figure 2. Time Line of Converter Box Subsidy Program.

WHILE MOST TELEVISION STATIONS ARE TRANSMITTING A DIGITAL SIGNAL, NUMEROUS TECHNICAL AND COORDINATION ISSUES REMAIN

The vast majority of broadcast television stations already broadcast a digital signal with many of these stations prepared to turn off their analog signal on February 17, 2009. However, a number of technical and coordination issues remain, such as antenna replacement and tower construction. In addition, cable and satellite television providers must coordinate with broadcasters to ensure that they can continue to receive and transmit the digital broadcast signals after the transition. While not required to cease analog broadcasting, some translator stations may choose to retransmit a digital signal but others will convert the digital signal to analog and continue to broadcast in analog after February 2009.

Broadcasters Face Technical and Coordination Issues

According to FCC, as of April 2007, approximately 93 percent of television broadcast stations were transmitting a digital signal. [7] FCC reports that nearly 1,200 of these stations already transmitting a digital signal have been authorized to continue to operate on their current digital channel after February 17, 2009. FCC states that these stations will have a relatively simple transition to their final post-transition digital operation. Additionally, FCC states that approximately 750 of these stations may now already be or are very close to being ready for their post-transition operations and will simply have to turn off their analog signal. For example, managers representing six television broadcast stations that we interviewed said that they face no major transition issues between by February 17, 2009, and will only have to turn off their analog signal.

However, as discussed below, stations may encounter challenges in completing their digital transition such as, (1) antenna and equipment replacement or relocation, (2) tower construction, (3) channel relocation, and (4) coordination with Canadian and Mexican governments.

Issues with antenna and equipment replacement or relocation. One of the major tasks that many television stations have to complete to build out their post-transition digital facilities is to install a digital antenna on the top of the broadcast tower, where the analog antenna resides. According to a broadcast industry official, many stations need to have their digital antenna at the top of the tower in order to fully replicate the area that their analog service covers. The broadcast industry official stated that stations have two options in placing their digital antenna at the top of the broadcast tower: (1) move the digital antenna to the top now, and buy a new side mounted analog antenna, which would ensure that the analog signal continues until it is switched off and that the digital signal would be at full power; or (2) keep the analog antenna at the top of the tower until it is turned off on February 17, 2009, then install the digital antenna at the top of the tower. The industry official stated that both options, however, present problems for broadcast stations. For the first option, stations may have to purchase a new analog antenna, which will only be used for a few months, and as a result of the analog antenna being side mounted, stations' analog broadcast coverage area would be reduced by 2 percent to 9 percent of the viewing market. Stations agreed that they could potentially have to reduce their analog service prior to the transition date. For example, the owner of a station in Minnesota commented that it may not be possible to complete the construction of its digital facilities without significantly disrupting its analog operation as well as its digital operations. The owner said the power of its analog signal would have to be significantly reduced before February 17, 2009, affecting a large number of its viewers. For the second option, problems include the digital signal not being at full power until later in the year, and getting the necessary authority to do this from FCC.

Further, broadcast stations have commented that the design, manufacture, and installation of new antennas can take months to complete. For example, a company that owns five television stations commented that it can take up to 6 months to design, order, receive and install a new antenna.

Even when stations do have their digital facilities fully operational, they may not broadcast their digital signal to the exact coverage area that their analog signal covered. For example, representatives from a commercial television station told us that in order for the stations to replicate its analog service contour, it had to reduce coverage for part of its digital contour. As a result, the station representatives said that the digital signal will reach 15,000 fewer people and that while many of these homes will have cable and satellite to still receive the station's signal, some will not. As shown in figure 3, the digital signal coverage of a station can differ from its analog signal coverage. Consequently, homes residing in the light shaded areas relying on over-the-air signals might not be able to receive the digital broadcast signals.

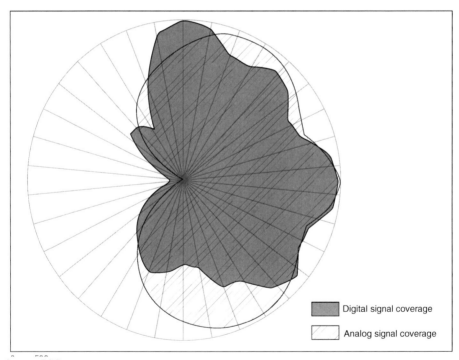

Source: FCC.

Figure 3. Example of a Station's Digital Signal Coverage Compared to Analog Signal Coverage

FCC has acknowledged that a reduction or termination of analog service may be necessary if maintaining full analog coverage hinders the construction and operation of digital facilities. FCC officials told us that some loss of analog service is part of a tradeoff needed to ensure the entire transition is as smooth as possible. FCC officials also said it is difficult to replicate an existing signal contour, and is almost impossible to exactly replicate a pattern. FCC stated that it is not always in the best interest of the public to have a digital signal fully replicate the analog signal because a digital signal can cause serious interference to nearby stations. Further, FCC said that, in some instances, while contour shifting may result in some viewers losing a station's signal, other homes might gain the signal of a station. For example, FCC said contour shifting might disenfranchise 500 people in one area, but cover a new area with 10,000 people.

Issues with tower construction. According to FCC, a station that must change its DTV tower locations may face considerable challenges, especially if the station must construct a new tower. FCC states that such stations must consider whether there are any existing towers that can be used or if a new tower must be constructed. FCC states that because of the lead times involved in purchasing or leasing land with appropriate federal government clearances, local and state zoning requirements, and varying timelines for designing the new tower, ordering equipment, delivery of equipment, and construction-related issues, stations must begin planning as soon as possible in order to transition by the deadline. According to a major television broadcast network, equipment manufacturing constraints and the limited number of tower crews and other key equipment installation resources available between now and the transition date will impede stations' movement to final digital channels by February 17, 2009. Additionally, any work on towers could be hampered by weather conditions for towers located in northern climates and on higher elevations. Television stations commented that working on towers in the winter months can be problematic, if not impossible. For example, a major broadcast network commented that many station transmitting sites are not readily accessible during the winter, especially to cranes and other heavy equipment necessary for tower rigging and equipment installation. In fact, the broadcaster commented that snow and ice make one of its stations accessible only by a special vehicle from October until March and another of its sites can only be reached by special vehicle until April.

Issues with channel relocation. According to FCC, approximately 600 stations will have to move to a different channel once the transition is complete. Some of these stations are broadcasting on a temporary digital channel and plan to relocate this digital channel back to their current analog channel. For example, one station we visited has its digital signal on channel 16 but plans to relocate the digital signal to channel 9, which is the station's current analog channel and the channel number people recognize for that station. Other stations will have to move to a completely new channel once the transition is complete. According to a broadcast industry association representative, television stations moving to another channel will face some technical challenges. For example, the broadcast representative stated that stations moving to another channel could cause interference for their neighboring channels if they move too early or if the neighboring channel moves too late. He estimated that there could be interference issues for up to 300 stations and stressed the need for coordination to minimize interference issues. Additionally, some stations broadcasting an analog signal do not have a paired digital channel and plan to "flash cut" to their digital channel by February 17, 2009.[8] According to FCC, "flash cutting" may present challenges since it will involve stations ending their analog television operations and beginning their digital television operations on their current analog channel and, in some cases, will require that a station change to a new channel to be fully operational.

Coordination issues with Canadian and Mexican governments. Another challenge for some stations located along the northern and southern borders of the United States is reaching agreements with Canadian and Mexican governments on the coverage of their digital signals that cross the border. According to FCC, some stations may still have unresolved coordination issues with Canadian and Mexican governments. Stations have commented that coordination issues with Canadian and Mexican governments might affect their ability to finalize their digital operations. For example, a company that operates several stations near the Canadian border commented that uncertainty about the stations' final digital signal coverage are preventing it from ordering equipment, scheduling tower crews and making necessary changes to its transmitter buildings. The company stated that if coordination issues cannot be resolved, the stations would face significant additional costs in constructing their digital facilities and could result in two of its stations discontinuing operations as full power stations and rather, operate as low power stations. Another station located near the Mexican border commented that the station's digital channel allotment could result in the Mexican government delaying or denying any request for coordination due to concerns about interference with a station on the Mexican side of the border. The station comments that any delay in coordination will result in the station not having sufficient time to construct its digital facilities. FCC officials told us that they are in discussions with Canadian and Mexican governments to resolve any coordination issues and expect to the discussions to be completed by January 2008. However, FCC has commented that if there are situations where international coordination cannot be obtained, stations may have to broadcast to a smaller coverage area.

Cable and Satellite Television Providers Must Coordinate with Broadcasters to Ensure They Continue to Receive Broadcast Signals

Cable and satellite television providers face fewer challenges than broadcasters with the DTV transition, however, there are technical issues that need to be resolved to ensure they can provide digital broadcast signals to their subscribers. For cable, FCC recently indicated its intent to require cable to either carry both a digital and analog signal, often referred to as a "dual carriage" requirement, or carry only the digital signal provided all subscribers can view the signal.[9] FCC further indicated its intent to require that high definition broadcast signals continue to be carried in high definition format. According to FCC, this will ensure all cable subscribers are able to view broadcast signals on their current televisions –whether analog or digital. We heard from cable providers that there are key technical challenges needing to be resolved prior to the transition. As previously noted, the technical and coordination issues facing the broadcasters can vary from station to station, with some stations moving to a new channel or changing the coverage area of their broadcast signal. As a result, cable providers told us there is uncertainty whether its cable head-ends will continue to receive the broadcast signals.[10] For example, if a broadcaster's digital coverage area differs from its analog coverage area, there is a possibility the cable head-end will no longer be able to receive that signal. One cable provider told us this could be particularly problematic in smaller markets where head-ends rely on over-the-air broadcast to pull in the broadcast signals. Cable providers will have to coordinate with local broadcasters to ensure cable continues to receive local broadcast feeds. In particular, we heard that cable providers need the coverage areas, or signal contour maps, from broadcast stations as soon as possible to help them identify problem areas. One cable provider we spoke with indicated based on potential changing signal coverage areas, it might need to reposition its antennas or otherwise update its head-ends so that they can continue to receive the broadcast signals. Since the cable provider has hundreds of head-ends, it could be time consuming to update them. Furthermore, this cable provider emphasized concerns with clearing enough bandwidth for the "dual carriage" requirements. While this should not be a major issue in the bigger markets, it could be problematic in many of the smaller markets where there is no viable technological solution for dealing with these requirements on bandwidth.

The satellite television providers we talked to anticipate no technical issues that will impact their subscribers' viewable broadcast signals following the transition date. However, similar to cable, satellite providers have concerns about broadcasters' coverage area changing such that the satellite receiving stations will fall out of the coverage area resulting in a lost or poorly received broadcast signal. Since satellite television operates on a national platform, the satellite providers will have to coordinate with all broadcast stations carried nationally.[11] To better coordinate and be better prepared for the DTV transition, both cable and satellite providers support broadcast stations making their transition plans public. Cable and satellite providers indicated advanced planning will allow them adequate time to make technical modifications to their systems, such as updating their receiving equipment and testing signal strength and reception.

Owners of Translator Stations Will Need to Take Action in Order for Viewers to Continue to Receive Translator Signals

Unlike full power broadcast television stations, the February 17, 2009 deadline to cease analog broadcasting does not apply to translator stations.[12] However, since translator stations retransmit signals from full power broadcast stations, owners of these stations will need to take action to ensure broadcast signals continue to reach viewers. Translator stations can either transition to digital or take the digital signal and convert it to analog before transmitting it to their viewers. Those stations transitioning to digital have two options; they can cease analog transmission and begin operation of new digital transmitting equipment on the same date, or they can operate a digital companion channel allowing them to deliver both analog and digital signals. According to a broadcast industry association, there are currently several hundred companion digital channels operating, and FCC is not presently allowing these stations to cease analog operation even though they are transmitting a digital signal. However, many translator stations will continue to transmit an analog signal beyond the full-power analog shutdown date. One broadcast industry association representative told us that although many translators will likely have obtained the hardware to operate with the digital input signal by the transition date, some stations will not have the necessary equipment.

If a translator station decides to convert the digital signal to analog and retransmit the signal, there is a possibility they will not reach those viewers who have purchased set-top converter boxes. According to a broadcast industry association, there are some instances where translator stations serve communities that receive at least one full-power television station, which would necessitate those over-the-air viewers to obtain a converter box. Since these areas will continue receiving both digital and analog signals, there is concern that those people who buy a set-top converter box that does not have analog pass through will have to turn them off or have an external bypass arrangement to allow for over-the-air signals to pass through their analog sets.

OUR FUTURE WORK WILL FOCUS ON THE PROGRESS OF THE DTV TRANSITION

We have work planned to assess the progress of the DTV transition. To accomplish this, we will continue to monitor public and private sector efforts related to the transition, including consumer outreach, the converter box subsidy program, and technical issues. Specifically, we will review consumer education programs and plan to conduct a series of consumer surveys throughout the year prior to the transition date. The surveys we conduct will be aimed at determining the population that will be affected by the DTV transition and the public awareness of the transition. In determining the affected population, we will look at the percent of the population relying on over-the-air broadcasts for their primary television, as well as the percent of the population with non-primary televisions being used to watch over-the-air television. Additionally, we will review the demographic characteristics of the affected population to determine what groups might be most disrupted by the transition. We will survey for public awareness of the DTV transition, and specific knowledge of the transition, such as when the transition will take place. We will seek to determine the level of public awareness of those who will be affected by the transition and awareness of the converter box subsidy program and other options for viewing digital signals after the transition. We plan to report on changes in consumer awareness over time by conducting surveys throughout the transition process. Furthermore, we will continue to monitor government and industry consumer education efforts and will analyze the efforts compared with key practices for consumer outreach. We will also monitor the outcome of FCC's notices of proposed rulemaking regarding the transition and collect details on IBM's consumer education plan as they become available. To monitor the implementation of the converter box subsidy program, we plan to continue reviewing the steps taken by NTIA and IBM in administering the subsidy program. In addition, we plan to survey broadcasters to obtain their perspectives on the technical issues that must be addressed prior to the DTV transition date.

> Mr. Chairman, this concludes my prepared statement. I would be happy to respond to any questions you or other Members of the Committee may have at this time.

REFERENCES

[1]   The radiofrequency spectrum is the part of the natural spectrum of electromagnetic radiation lying below 300 gigahertz. It is the medium that makes possible wireless communications, including cellular and paging services, radio and television broadcasting, radar, and satellite-based services.

[2]   NTIA established technical and performance specifications that converter boxes must meet to be eligible for the coupon program.

[3]   While NTIA is not an official Coalition member, the agency has been participating in Coalition activities since its inception. The Coalition, as well as FCC and NTIA, have created Web sites providing information on the DTV transition and converter box subsidy program. These Web sites are available for viewing at the following addresses: www.dtvtransition.org and www.dtv.gov and http://www.ntia.doc.gov/otiahome/dtv/.

[4] GAO, *Telecommunications: German DTV Transition Differs from U.S. Transition in Many Respects, but Certain Key Challenges Are Similar*, GAO-04-926T (Washington D.C.: July 21, 2004).

[5] GAO, *Results-Oriented Government: Practices That Can Help Enhance and Sustain Collaboration among Federal Agencies*, GAO-06-15 (Washington, D.C.: October 21, 2005).

[6] Point of sale systems record purchases, payments, returns, and exchanges, as well as send the individual transactions to the company's internal inventory and accounting systems. They can also include an external component of 'in real time' communication with financial institutions, merchant banks, or other sources to identify the validity of the method of payment and authorize utilization of that method (credit card, debit card, gift card, check, etc).

[7] As of April 2, 2007, 1,603 of the approximate 1,722 licensed television stations broadcast a digital signal. Of the stations broadcasting a digital signal, 1,136 represent commercial licensed stations.

[8] According to FCC, "flash-cut" refers to the situation where a station gives up its pre-transition digital channel and transitions to digital service using its analog channel or a newly allotted channel.

[9] The FCC rules were adopted on September 11, 2007, but as of October 11, 2007, the final ruling had yet to be published.

[10] Cable providers receive the local broadcast signals to their head-ends, while satellite providers receive the local broadcast signals at local receive facilities. This signal can be received by the providers either over-the-air, across fiber, by microwave antenna, or other means. Over-the-air signals could be lost completely based on changes to the broadcast stations antenna placement or structure, but fiber and other means of receiving the broadcast signal may require changes in equipment.

[11] The two satellite television providers, EchoStar and DIRECTV, retransmit 1,500 local broadcast signals and 1,200 local broadcast signals, respectively.

[12] Most of the approximately 5,000 translator stations operate in the mountainous western regions of the country and are often used to deliver the only off-air television service available in rural communities. Although some translator stations are owned by full-power stations, many are either owned or rely on support from a local government.

In: Digital Television: On the Threshold
Editor: Mark L. Goldstein, pp. 21-33

ISBN: 978-1-60456-693-2
© 2008 Nova Science Publishers, Inc.

Chapter 2

DIGITAL TELEVISION TRANSITION PRELIMINARY INFORMATION ON INITIAL CONSUMER EDUCATION EFFORTS[*]

Government Accountability Office

WHY GAO DID THIS STUDY

On February 17, 2009, federal law requires all full-power television stations in the United States to cease analog broadcasting and broadcast digital-only transmissions, often referred to as the digital television (DTV) transition. Federal law also requires the National Telecommunications and Information Administration (NTIA) to create a program that subsidizes consumers' purchases of digital-to- analog converter boxes. After the transition, households with analog sets that rely on over-the-air broadcast signals must take action or they will lose television service, but some households might not be aware of this potential disruption. This testimony provides preliminary information on (1) the consumer education efforts currently underway, (2) education efforts being planned, (3) difficulties with the implementation of consumer education programs, and (4) ongoing GAO work on consumer education and awareness regarding the transition. GAO interviewed officials with the Federal Communications Commission (FCC) and NTIA. Further, GAO met with a wide variety of industry and other stakeholders involved with the transition, including members of the DTV Transition Coalition—a group of public and private

---

[*] This chapter is an excerpted, indexed edition of GAO Report GAO-07-1248T, Dated September 19, 2007

stakeholders, and experts on strategic communications. GAO discussed this testimony with FCC and NTIA officials and incorporated their comments.

WHAT GAO FOUND

A number of federal and private stakeholders have begun consumer education campaigns, with both independent and coordinated efforts underway. FCC has taken several steps to promote consumer awareness, such as launching a Web site, participating in events intended to educate the public, and requiring sellers of televisions to include consumer alerts on non-digital televisions. NTIA has created brochures in English and Spanish to provide the public information about its converter box subsidy program and is partnering with organizations to perform outreach to disadvantaged groups. Earlier this year, the DTV Transition Coalition was launched to help ensure that no consumer is left without broadcast television due to a lack of information. Over 160 private, public, and non-profit groups have joined the Coalition to coordinate consumer education efforts.

While widespread and comprehensive consumer education efforts have yet to be implemented, various efforts are currently being planned. FCC, NTIA, and private sector stakeholders have plans to further educate consumers as the DTV transition nears. For example, voluntary public service announcements to raise awareness of the transition are planned by industry groups and FCC is considering requiring broadcasters, manufacturers and cable and satellite providers to insert various messages and alerts in their products and programming. In addition, the converter box subsidy program will have a consumer education component. Because many education efforts are in the planning or early stages of implementation, it is too early to tell how effective these efforts will be.

Various factors make consumer education difficult. While private sector stakeholders are participating in outreach efforts, these actions are voluntary and therefore the government cannot be assured of the extent of private sector efforts. Strategic communications experts from industry, government, and academia identified potential challenges to a consumer education campaign, including (1) prioritizing limited resources to target the right audience, (2) educating consumers to help protect them from making unnecessary purchases, (3) reaching underserved populations, and (4) aligning stakeholders to form a consistent, coordinated effort.

GAO has work planned to assess the progress of consumer awareness. In particular, GAO plans to conduct a series of surveys to determine the population affected by the DTV transition, levels of awareness about the transition, and demographic information about the affected population. Throughout the transition, GAO will continue to monitor government and industry education efforts and analyze these efforts relative to best practices for consumer education campaigns. GAO plans to review the government's responsibility for consumer education, monitor the outcome of FCC's rulemaking related to consumer education, and collect details of the consumer education component of the converter box subsidy program.

Mr. Chairman and Members of the Committee:

I am pleased to be here today to report on our work for the House Energy and Commerce committee and this committee on the progress made in consumer education efforts for the digital television (DTV) transition. We are currently finalizing a report on initial public and private sector efforts underway to implement the transition; as such, the findings that I am reporting to the Committee today are preliminary in nature and principally related to consumer education and outreach programs.

A primary goal of the DTV transition is for the federal government to reclaim spectrum[1] that broadcasters currently use to provide analog television signals. The spectrum that the federal government will reclaim at the end of the transition is considered highly valuable because of its particular technical properties. In all, the DTV transition will free up 108 megahertz (MHz) of spectrum. The Federal Communications Commission (FCC) has reallocated 24 MHz of the spectrum that will be recovered for public safety purposes, which became a higher priority following the terrorist attacks of September 11, 2001. FCC will auction the remaining spectrum for commercial purposes, with the resulting proceeds allocated for, among other things, reducing the federal deficit.

The Digital Television Transition and Public Safety Act of 2005 mandates the cessation of analog television broadcast signals on February 17, 2009. After that date, households that had previously viewed television on analog sets solely through the reception of over-the-air signals must take action to ensure that they have the necessary equipment, such as a digital-to-analog converter box, or subscription video service to be able to view the digital broadcast signals. If they do not take such action, they will lose the ability to view the digital signals on their analog sets. The act also directed the National Telecommunications and Information Administration (NTIA) to establish a $1.5 billion program through which households can obtain coupons for the purchase of digital-to-analog converter boxes. NTIA issued a final rule that adopted regulations to implement the converter box subsidy program, and in August 2007, selected IBM Corporation (IBM) to administer the program. Beginning January 1, 2008, households can request up to two $40 coupons toward the purchase of eligible[2] digital-to-analog converter boxes.

Three private sector groups have asserted various estimates of the number of households that rely solely on over-the-air television. While one group estimates that 11 percent of households rely on over-the-air broadcasts, another group's estimate is 16 percent of households, and a third group's estimate is 20 percent of households. Further, private sector estimates claim an additional 5 percent to 27 percent of households that subscribe to cable or satellite television have at least one television set that receives an over-the-air signal. One group asserted that households that rely on over-the-air broadcasts are disproportionately comprised of older citizens than other households. Although it is unclear what percentage of households that rely exclusively on over-the-air broadcasts use analog rather than digital television sets, millions of those households potentially stand to be left without any television service unless they take action. To help the public understand the DTV transition and the various options they have, consumer education and awareness programs are underway and additional programs are being planned.

While there are many steps necessary to successfully complete the DTV transition, my testimony today will focus on consumer education and awareness. In particular, I will discuss (1) consumer education efforts currently underway, (2) education efforts and programs being planned, (3) the difficulties that may arise in the implementation of such programs, and (4) ongoing work on DTV consumer education and awareness that we will undertake.

To meet these objectives, we interviewed officials with FCC and NTIA, as well as a wide variety of industry and other private stakeholders, such as broadcasters, manufacturers, retailers, and consumer advocacy groups. Further, we consulted strategic communications experts representing public, private, and academic organizations to identify potential challenges that might obstruct consumer education efforts. We performed our review from January 2007 through August 2007 in accordance with generally accepted government auditing standards. We discussed this testimony with FCC and NTIA officials to obtain their comments. FCC and NTIA provided additional information that we incorporated where appropriate.

IN SUMMARY

- Several federal and private stakeholders have begun consumer education campaigns, with both independent and coordinated efforts underway. FCC and NTIA have been involved in consumer education and awareness programs and some private sector organizations are voluntarily taking the lead on outreach efforts. For example, FCC has launched a Web site (DTV.gov) and NTIA has begun outreach efforts to groups most likely to lose all television service as a result of the transition—including at-risk groups such as the elderly—with "information sheets" and brochures. Private, public, and nonprofit groups have joined together to form the DTV Transition Coalition to coordinate on consumer education efforts and messages.

- Widespread and comprehensive consumer education efforts have yet to be implemented, but additional efforts are currently being planned both for the general population and at-risk groups. FCC, NTIA, and private sector stakeholders have plans to further educate consumers as the transition nears. FCC solicited comments on proposed consumer education programs, including potentially requiring television broadcasters to conduct on-air consumer education efforts. The proposals also include potential requirements for industry to report on the status of their specific consumer outreach efforts, including those efforts targeted to at-risk groups. Included in NTIA's converter box subsidy program is a consumer education component—the details of which have not been made public. Some organizations, such as the DTV Transition Coalition and various industry trade associations, are planning information and education campaigns and some groups are planning to broadcast public service announcements.

- Despite the efforts currently underway and those being planned, difficulties remain in the implementation of consumer education programs. While private sector organizations are conducting outreach efforts, these actions are voluntary and therefore the government cannot be assured of the extent of private sector efforts. Strategic communications experts from industry, government, and academia identified potential challenges to a consumer education campaign, including (1) prioritizing limited resources to target the right audience for an adequate period of time, (2) educating consumers who do not necessarily need to take action, (3) reaching underserved populations, such as the elderly and disabled, and (4) aligning stakeholders to form a consistent, coordinated effort.

- In our ongoing work for the House Energy and Commerce committee and this committee, we plan on reporting on the progress of consumer education and awareness about the DTV transition throughout the upcoming transition period. For example, we will continue to monitor consumer education programs and plan to conduct a series of consumer surveys throughout the year prior to the transition date. These surveys will be aimed at estimating the population that will be affected by the DTV transition and the public awareness of the transition. We will estimate the percent of the population relying on over-the-air broadcasts, as well as demographic characteristics of the affected population to determine what groups might be most disrupted by the transition. We will report on changes in consumer awareness over time based on surveys we plan to conduct throughout the transition process. In addition, throughout the transition process, we will continue to assess government and industry consumer education efforts and analyze the efforts compared with key practices for consumer outreach.

BACKGROUND

The United States is currently undergoing a transition from analog to digital broadcast television, often referred to as the DTV transition. The transition will enable the government to allocate valuable spectrum from analog broadcast to public safety and other purposes. Further, digital transmission of television signals provides several advantages compared to analog transmission, such as enabling better quality picture and sound reception as well as using the radiofrequency spectrum more efficiently than analog transmission. With traditional analog technology, pictures and sounds are converted into "waveform" electrical signals for transmission through the radiofrequency spectrum, while digital technology converts these pictures and sounds into a stream of digits consisting of zeros and ones for transmission.

The Digital Television Transition and Public Safety Act of 2005 addresses the responsibilities of two federal agencies—FCC and NTIA—related to the DTV transition. The act directs FCC to require full-power television stations to cease analog broadcasting and to broadcast solely digital transmissions after February 17, 2009. As we have previously reported, households with analog televisions that rely solely on over-the-air television signals received through a rooftop antenna or indoor antenna must take action to be able to view digital broadcast signals after the termination of analog broadcasts. Options available to these households include (1) purchasing a digital television set that includes a tuner capable of receiving, processing, and displaying a digital signal; (2) purchasing a digital-to-analog converter box, which converts the digital broadcast signals to analog so they can be viewed on an existing analog set; or (3) subscribing to a cable, satellite, or other service to eliminate the need to acquire a digital-to-analog converter box. The act also directed NTIA to establish a $1.5 billion subsidy program through which households can obtain coupons toward the purchase of digital-to-analog converter boxes. The last day for consumers to request coupons is March 31, 2009, and coupons can be redeemed through July 9, 2009. As required by law, all coupons expire 90 days after issuance. Consumers can redeem their coupons at participating retailers (both "brick and mortar" and online) for eligible converter boxes.

To help inform consumers about the transition, eight private sector organizations launched the DTV Transition Coalition in February 2007. These eight organizations are the Association for Maximum Service Television, Association of Public Television Stations, Consumer Electronics Association, Consumer Electronic Retailers Coalition, Leadership Conference on Civil Rights, LG Electronics, National Association of Broadcasters, and the National Cable and Telecommunications Association. These founding organizations comprise the Coalition's steering committee and make decisions on behalf of the Coalition. To better represent the interests of at-risk or underserved populations—such as the elderly—AARP later joined the steering committee. The Coalition's mission is to ensure that no consumer is left without broadcast television due to a lack of information about the transition. Currently, the Coalition has over 160 member organizations comprised of business, trade and industry groups, as well as FCC.[3]

Recent surveys conducted by industry trade associations indicate that consumer awareness of the digital transition is low. The Association for Public Television Stations reported in January 2007 that 61 percent of participants surveyed had "no idea" that the transition was taking place. Another study conducted by the National Association of Broadcasters focused on households that primarily receive their television signals over-the-air—and will therefore be most affected by the transition—and reported that 57 percent of those surveyed were not aware of the transition. Both surveys found that most people with some awareness of the transition had limited awareness of the date the transition will take place.

FEDERAL GOVERNMENT AND PRIVATE STAKEHOLDER CONSUMER EDUCATION EFFORTS ARE UNDERWAY

Federal and private stakeholders are making progress in educating consumers about the DTV transition, with both independent and coordinated efforts underway. FCC and NTIA have been involved in consumer education and awareness programs and some private sector organizations are voluntarily taking the lead on outreach efforts.

FCC has taken several steps toward educating consumers about the transition. For example, FCC has launched a Web site (DTV.gov), which, among other things, provides background information on the DTV transition and answers common consumer questions. In addition, FCC has met with some industry groups, consumer groups, and other government agencies and participated in public events intended to educate audiences about the transition. Moreover, in April 2007, FCC adopted a rule requiring all sellers of television-receiving equipment that does not include a digital tuner to prominently display a consumer alert that such devices will require a converter box to receive over-the-air broadcast television after February 17, 2009. To ensure that retailers are in compliance, FCC staff have inspected over 1,000 retail stores and Web sites and issued over 250 citations with potential fines exceeding $3 million. In addition, FCC has issued notices to television manufacturers with potential fines over $2.5 million for importing televisions without digital tuners. In June 2007, FCC announced that it had re-chartered an intergovernmental advisory committee comprised of 15 representatives from local, state, and tribal governments to help it address, among other things, consumer education about the DTV transition. Similarly, it re-chartered a consumer advisory committee that will also make recommendations to FCC about the transition on behalf of consumers, with specific representation for people with disabilities and other underserved or at-risk populations.

NTIA has also taken initial steps towards educating consumers about the transition. NTIA has statutory responsibility for the converter box subsidy program, for which Congress appropriated up to $5 million for education efforts. According to NTIA, its education efforts are focused on the subsidy program and more specifically on five groups most likely to lose all television service as a result of the transition: (1)

senior citizens, (2) the economically disadvantaged, (3) rural residents, (4) people with disabilities, and (5) minorities. According to NTIA, it has begun outreach efforts to these groups through partnerships with private organizations as well as other federal agencies. Also, it has created "information sheets" for consumers, retailers, and manufacturers that outline the subsidy program and are available on its Web site. NTIA said it has provided informational brochures in English and Spanish to the public and provided a copy to every member of Congress and federal agencies that serve some of the populations noted above. The agency also created a consumer hotline that provides information about the transition in English and Spanish, and TTY numbers that provide information in English and Spanish to the hearing impaired. In addition, in August 2007, NTIA contracted with IBM to implement the broad consumer education component about the program.

On a voluntary basis, some private stakeholders have begun implementing measures to inform consumers about the DTV transition. As previously mentioned, one such private-sector led effort is the DTV Transition Coalition, which has developed and consumer tested various messages about the transition, using surveys and focus groups of the affected consumers—the general population, senior citizens, minority groups, and over-the-air analog television households—to understand what messages are most effective in informing them about the transition. Subsequently, the Coalition said it agreed upon one concise message that includes information about the transition itself, the rationale for the transition, and the ways consumers can effectively switch to DTV. In particular, the Coalition suggests consumers can prepare for the transition by purchasing a DTV converter box, purchasing a new television set with a built in digital tuner, or subscribing to a pay television service such as cable, satellite, or telephone company video service provider. The Coalition said its member organizations will distribute this information to their constituents, including senior citizens, the disabled, and minority groups. The Coalition message will also be delivered to media outlets.

In addition to coordinated efforts within the Coalition, private sector organizations also have independent education efforts underway. For example, a number of industry associations host Web sites that inform consumers of, among other things, common consumer questions about the transition, how to check if the television they own is digital-ready, and how to dispose of analog television sets. One national retailer told us that it added a feature to its registers so that when a consumer purchases an analog television, a message about the transition is printed on the bottom of the receipt.

MANY CONSUMER EDUCATION EFFORTS ARE STILL IN THE PLANNING STAGES AND HAVE NOT BEEN WIDELY IMPLEMENTED

Widespread and comprehensive consumer education efforts have yet to be implemented, but additional efforts are currently being planned. FCC, NTIA, and private sector stakeholders have plans to further educate consumers as the digital transition nears. The converter box subsidy program, to be administered by NTIA, will also have a consumer education component implemented by its contractor, IBM. Because many education efforts are in the planning or initial stages of implementation, it is too early to tell how effective these efforts will be.

FCC has solicited input on proposed consumer education programs. In August 2007, in response to a letter containing proposals on advancing consumer education submitted by members of Congress, FCC released a notice of proposed rulemaking soliciting public comments. These proposals include requiring television broadcasters to conduct on-air consumer education efforts and regularly report on the status of these efforts, requiring cable and satellite providers to insert periodic notices in customers' bills about the transition and their future viewing options, and requiring manufacturers to include information on the transition with any television set or related device they import or distribute in the United States. Each of the requirements mentions civil penalties for noncompliance. Another proposal on which FCC sought comment would have FCC work with NTIA to require that retailers participating in the converter box subsidy program detail their employee training and consumer information plans, as well as have FCC staff spot check the retailers for compliance. Also, FCC sought comments on a proposal requiring partners identified on FCC's DTV.gov Web site to report their specific consumer outreach efforts. The comment period on the notice of proposed rulemaking is scheduled to close on September 19, 2007; the period to file any rebuttal closes October 1, 2007.

NTIA also has not fully implemented education efforts about its subsidy program in large part because it is contracting out the consumer education component of its program. The contract was recently awarded in the middle of August 2007 to IBM and plans are in the development stage.

Many private sector consumer education efforts are in the planning stages and have yet to be fully implemented. Representatives from private sector organizations told us there are several reasons why they are waiting to fully launch their consumer education campaigns. In particular, some said they are trying to time their education efforts for maximum effectiveness and that they do not want to start too early and possibly lose the attention of consumers later on.

Another reason is that they are waiting for key events to occur, such as the availability of converter boxes in retail stores, so that education efforts can contain complete information. A number of nonprofit organizations told us that a lack of dedicated funding hampers their ability to educate and outreach to their constituents. Through its many member organizations, the DTV Transition Coalition intends to disseminate information about the transition in a variety of formats, including through presenting at conferences, creating media attention, and distributing informational materials to Congressional offices. The National Cable and Telecommunications Association has created public service announcements about the transition in both Spanish and English, which will be aired by cable operators and networks in markets throughout the country in the fall of 2007. The National Association of Broadcasters also has plans to launch a public service announcement campaign related to the transition by the end of 2007, which will air on its local television broadcasting affiliates, independent stations, and broadcast networks.

DIFFICULTIES REMAIN IN THE IMPLEMENTATION OF CONSUMER EDUCATION PROGRAMS

Despite efforts currently underway and those being planned, difficulties remain in the implementation of consumer education programs. Private sector organizations are participating in outreach efforts, but these actions are voluntary and therefore the government cannot be assured of the extent of private sector efforts. Moreover, given the different interests represented by industry stakeholders, messages directed at consumers vary and might lead to confusion. For example, in addition to providing information about why the transition is occurring, some industry stakeholders have incentives to provide consumers with information on a wide host of technology equipment or services that consumers could purchase, at varying costs. Advocates for the elderly, disabled, and non-English speaking households told us that they are concerned that their members will become confused by the options and end up purchasing equipment they do not need or more expensive equipment than necessary to maintain their television viewing.

Further, we heard from strategic communication experts from industry, government, and academia that potential challenges might obstruct consumer education efforts. In particular, the experts and others highlighted several challenges:

- *Prioritizing limited resources.* With limited time and financial resources, it is likely to be a challenge for stakeholders to determine how best to allocate those resources within the campaign—for example, whether to target a smaller audience over a set period of time, versus targeting a broader audience over a shorter period of time. This is applicable because, according to industry stakeholders, there may be specific groups that are more vulnerable than others to losing television service.

- *Educating consumers who do not necessarily need to take action.* Many of the outreach efforts will be focused on educating consumers on what to do to keep their television sets from going dark after the termination of analog broadcasts. However, a large proportion of U.S. households will not need to do anything—for example, because they have cable or satellite television service that will enable their analog set to continue to display programming. Because many messages focus on the actions that households that rely on over-the-air analog broadcasting need to take, consumers unaffected by the transition might become confused and purchase equipment they do not need. In our past work looking at a similar digital transition in Germany, we have described this potential confusion to cable and satellite households as a challenge of educating consumers about the transition.

- *Reaching underserved populations.* Conveying the message to underserved populations, such as senior citizens, the disabled, those residing in rural areas, or non-English speaking households, will provide an added challenge. Many groups reaching out to consumers about the transition are doing so on Web sites, which may not be available to people who lack Internet access or are less technically savvy. Another challenge is providing information in a wide variety of formats, such as in different languages for non-English speaking consumers and in text, video, voice, and Braille for the disabled. Overall, a challenge of consumer education is that those households in need of taking action may be the least likely to be aware of the transition.

- *Aligning stakeholders.* Industry representatives also noted the challenge of aligning stakeholders—some of whom are natural competitors—to work together. In our past work, we have reported that federal agencies engaged in collaborative efforts—such as the transition—need to create the means to monitor and evaluate their efforts to enable them to identify areas for improvement. Reporting on these activities can help key decision makers within the agencies, as well as clients and stakeholders, to obtain feedback for improving both policy and operational effectiveness. Some progress in aligning stakeholders, such as the formation of the DTV Transition Coalition, has been made, but some stakeholders may have competing interests. For example, recent announcements produced by the National Cable and Telecommunications Association invoke the DTV transition, but ultimately promote the role of cable television in the transition.

OUR FUTURE WORK WILL FOCUS ON CONSUMER AWARENESS OF THE DTV TRANSITION

In our ongoing work for the House Energy and Commerce committee and this committee, we plan to assess the progress of consumer education and awareness about the DTV transition. We will continue to monitor consumer education programs and plan to conduct a series of consumer surveys throughout the year prior to the transition date. These surveys will be aimed at determining the population that will be affected by the DTV transition and the public awareness of the transition. In determining the affected population, we will look at the percent of the population relying on over-the-air broadcasts for their primary television, as well as the percent of the population with non-primary televisions being used to watch over-the-air television. Additionally, we will review the demographic characteristics of the affected population to determine what groups might be most disrupted by the transition. We will survey for public awareness of the DTV transition, and specific knowledge of the transition, such as when the transition will take place. We will seek to determine the level of public awareness of those who will be affected by the transition and awareness of the converter box subsidy program and other options for viewing digital signals after the transition. We plan to report on changes in consumer awareness over time by conducting surveys throughout the transition process.

Furthermore, we will continue to assess government and industry consumer education efforts and will analyze the efforts compared with key practices for consumer outreach. We will review the government's responsibility for consumer education, monitor the outcome of FCC's notices of proposed rulemaking regarding the transition, and collect details on IBM's consumer education plan as they become available.

Mr. Chairman, this concludes my prepared statement. I would be happy to respond to any questions you or other Members of the Committee may have at this time.

REFERENCES

[1] The radiofrequency spectrum is the part of the natural spectrum of electromagnetic radiation lying below 300 gigahertz. It is the medium that makes possible wireless communications, including cellular and paging services, radio and television broadcasting, radar, and satellite-based services.

[2] NTIA established technical and performance specifications that converter boxes must meet to be eligible for the coupon program.

[3] While NTIA is not an official Coalition member, the agency has been participating in Coalition activities since its inception. The Coalition, as well as FCC and NTIA, have created Web sites providing information on the DTV transition and converter box subsidy program. These Web sites are available for viewing at the following addresses: www.dtvtransition.org, www.dtv.gov, www.ntia.doc.gov/dtvcoupon/index.html.

In: Digital Television: On the Threshold
Editor: Mark L. Goldstein, pp. 35-71

ISBN: 978-1-60456-693-2
© 2008 Nova Science Publishers, Inc.

Chapter 3

DIGITAL TELEVISION TRANSITION INCREASED FEDERAL PLANNING AND RISK MANAGEMENT COULD FURTHER FACILITATE THE DTV TRANSITION[*]

Government Accountability Office

WHY GAO DID THIS STUDY

The Digital Television Transition and Public Safety Act of 2005 requires all full-power television stations to cease analog broadcasting by February 17, 2009. Following this digital television transition, consumers who receive over-the-air television signals on analog sets will need to take action to be able to view digital broadcasts. The act also requires the National Telecommunications and Information Administration (NTIA) to create a program that subsidizes consumers' purchases of digital-to-analog converter boxes. This requested report examines progress made (1) by federal entities and others in facilitating the transition, (2) in educating consumers on the transition, and (3) in implementing the converter box subsidy program. GAO reviewed legal, agency, and industry documents; interviewed public, private, and other stakeholders; and convened an expert panel focused on consumer outreach.

---

[*] This chapter is an excerpted, indexed edition of GAO report GAO-08-43, Dated November 2007

WHAT GAO RECOMMENDS

GAO recommends that FCC, in conjunction with public and private stakeholders, develop a comprehensive plan for the various aspects of the DTV transition. In commenting on this report, FCC and the Department of Commerce (which contains NTIA) noted the steps they had taken to facilitate the transition, but neither indicated whether they agreed or disagreed with the recommendation. A more detailed discussion of their comments is in our report.

WHAT GAO FOUND

The Federal Communications Commission (FCC) and NTIA, in conjunction with other stakeholders, have taken actions to facilitate the digital television (DTV) transition. FCC has primary responsibility to regulate the broadcast television industry and, as such, has set deadlines for broadcasters to upgrade station equipment and conducted periodic reviews related to the transition. NTIA has issued a contract for services related to its converter box subsidy program. Industry stakeholders, including broadcasters, have begun to prepare for the transition. Despite these efforts, GAO found no comprehensive plan or strategy to measure progress and results. Such planning includes managing and mitigating risks, which can help organizations identify potential problems before they occur and target limited resources. GAO has reported on the benefits of risk management in helping organizations involved in high stakes efforts similar to the DTV transition.

FCC, NTIA, industry, and other private sector stakeholders have made progress in educating consumers about the DTV transition, but these efforts are mostly in the planning phase, and challenges remain. Both FCC and NTIA have developed informational materials on the transition and begun reaching out to consumer and stakeholder groups. Private sector stakeholders are leading consumer outreach efforts on a voluntary basis. This includes developing a coalition of over 160 business, trade, and other organizations committed to providing consumers with information about the transition; planning public service announcements; developing Web sites; and encouraging media coverage. An expert panel GAO convened identified key practices for consumer education planning, including coordinating among stakeholders, constructing consistent messages, researching target audiences, and establishing metrics to measure success. The expert panel also noted that potential challenges for consumer outreach include prioritizing limited resources, educating consumers who do not necessarily need to take action, and reaching underserved populations. It remains unclear whether public-private sector interaction can ensure a consistent message to prevent consumer confusion.

NTIA has made progress in implementing a subsidy program for converter boxes, but the program faces challenges. The current program allows households to request up to two $40 coupons toward the purchase of eligible converter boxes. While the program's outcome depends on the ability of NTIA and its contractor to encourage and coordinate the voluntary participation of retailers and manufacturers, NTIA remains ultimately responsible for the program. There is also uncertainty regarding retailer readiness and participation in the program, as well as potential challenges related to inventory planning. If retailers' participation is limited or delayed, consumers might face difficulties in redeeming their coupons for converter boxes, without which some might lose access to television programming.

ABBREVIATIONS

ATSC	Advanced Television Systems Committee
CEA	Consumer Electronics Association
DOC	Department of Commerce
DTV	digital television
FCC	Federal Communications Commission
GAGAS	generally accepted government auditing standards
IBM	International Business Machines Corporation
MHz	megahertz
NOAA	National Oceanic and Atmospheric Administration
NTIA	National Telecommunications and Information Administration
NTSC	National Television Systems Committee
Y2K	Year 2000 Computer Conversion

November 19, 2007

Congressional Requesters

By February 17, 2009, federal law requires all full-power television stations in the United States to cease analog broadcasting and broadcast digital-only transmissions, often referred to as the digital television (DTV) transition. A primary goal of the DTV transition is for the federal government to reclaim spectrum[1] that broadcasters currently use to provide analog television signals. The spectrum that the federal government will reclaim at the end of the transition is considered highly valuable because of its particular technical properties. In all, the DTV transition will free up 108 megahertz (MHz) of spectrum because digital transmissions require less spectrum than analog transmissions. The Federal Communications Commission (FCC) has reallocated 24 MHz of the spectrum for public safety purposes, which became a higher priority following the terrorist attacks of September 11, 2001. FCC will auction the remaining spectrum for commercial purposes, the proceeds of which, Congress had determined, will in part be allocated toward reducing the federal deficit.[2]

After the DTV transition, consumers who rely exclusively on over-the-air television signals viewed on analog sets[3] will not be able to view broadcast programming, possibly including important news information or emergency alerts, unless they take action. In particular, these consumers could (1) purchase a television capable of processing digital signals;[4] (2) purchase a digital-to-analog converter box that converts the digital signals to analog signals and enables their display on an analog set; or (3) subscribe to cable, satellite, or other service that already converts digital signals into a format an analog receiver can process or will provide a remedy for their viewers. A number of governmental and private sector stakeholders are currently planning outreach efforts to educate consumers about this important transition to digital television. Furthermore, as required by the Digital Television Transition and Public Safety Act of 2005,[5] the National Telecommunications and Information Administration (NTIA), an agency of the U.S. Department of Commerce, created a digital-to-analog converter box subsidy program establishing that beginning January 1, 2008, households can request up to two $40 coupons toward the purchase of such converter boxes. In August 2007, NTIA contracted with International Business Machines Corporation (IBM) to provide services for the subsidy program. The implementation of this program, in addition to a widespread consumer education campaign, will require the coordination of government agencies, manufacturers, retailers, broadcasters, and public advocacy groups.

You asked us to provide information on the progress of the DTV transition. We reviewed the progress made (1) by federal entities, in conjunction with other stakeholders, in facilitating the transition; (2) in educating consumers about the transition and any related challenges; and (3) in implementing a subsidy program for converter boxes and any related challenges. We are also reviewing technical issues related to the DTV transition and will report on progress and challenges in these areas in the near future.

To meet these objectives, we reviewed relevant laws and regulations, agency strategic plans, budgets, time lines, public comments, proposed reporting requirements, and the NTIA contract for the converter box subsidy program to determine the nation's progress toward digital television. We interviewed officials with FCC and NTIA, as well as a wide variety of industry and other private sector stakeholders with an interest in the transition, such as broadcasters, retailers, manufacturers, and advocacy groups. We discussed their roles in the transition and obtained information on their involvement with consumer education efforts and the NTIA converter box subsidy program. Further, we convened a panel of 14 experts representing public, private, and academic organizations to identify key practices for conducting consumer education. A more detailed discussion of our objectives, scope, and methodology is provided in appendix I. We performed our review from January 2007 through August 2007 in accordance with generally accepted government auditing standards.

RESULTS IN BRIEF

FCC and NTIA, in conjunction with other stakeholders, have taken steps to facilitate the DTV transition. FCC has primary responsibility to regulate the television broadcast industry for the federal government and has taken a number of actions regarding the transition. For example, FCC has proposed and set deadlines to upgrade station equipment to send digital signals. In addition, FCC has conducted periodic reviews to report on transition progress and held a workshop for interested parties to discuss transition challenges and issues. NTIA has statutory responsibility for the converter box subsidy program, and it has issued a contract for certain services related to that program's operation. Private sector stakeholders, including broadcasters, manufacturers, and retailers have also begun preparing for the transition. Despite public-private sector interaction designed to help facilitate the transition, we found that no comprehensive plan exists for the DTV transition. Among other things, a comprehensive plan can detail milestones and key goals, which provide meaningful guidance for assigning and coordinating responsibilities and deadlines and measuring progress. Such planning also includes assessing, managing, and mitigating risks, which can help organizations to identify potential problems before they occur and target limited resources. We have previously reported on the benefits of managing risks, including assisting other organizations involved in high stakes efforts similar to the DTV transition. For example, we credited one federal agency's success in weathering the potential for critical computer system failures during the Year 2000 Computer Conversion (Y2K), in part, due to reducing risks to facilities, systems, programs, and services during the critical rollover.

FCC and NTIA, along with industry and other private sector stakeholders, have made progress in educating consumers about the DTV transition. For example, FCC and NTIA have developed informational materials on the transition and begun outreach directly to consumer and stakeholder groups. Both agencies are also involved with the Digital Television Transition Coalition, a group representing over 160 business, trade, grassroots, and other organizations whose purpose is to provide consumers with information about the transition. Private sector stakeholders are voluntarily taking the lead on planning public service announcements, developing Web sites, and garnering media coverage on the transition. While federal and private stakeholders have taken these initial steps, the initiative is still largely in the planning stages, and widespread efforts have yet to be implemented. Further, because of the number of public and private sector entities involved in consumer education efforts for the DTV transition as well as the timing, coordination, and content of the messages they produce, consumers might become confused over what steps, if any, are necessary to avoid disruptions to their television viewing after the transition date. During an expert panel we convened, communications experts identified challenges to consumer outreach, such as prioritizing limited resources and ensuring that certain at-risk populations receive the information they need. In addition, the panel identified the key components of a consumer education campaign, such as the need to clarify the roles and responsibilities of all stakeholders and the importance of developing a consistent, clear message. At the time of our report, it remains unclear whether there will be sufficient public-private sector interaction to ensure a consistent message to prevent confusion or unnecessary purchases on the part of consumers.

NTIA has made progress in implementing the converter box subsidy program, including soliciting stakeholder comments, meeting with industry participants, and selecting IBM in August 2007 to provide services for the program. Despite NTIA's progress in implementing the subsidy program, the program still faces certain challenges. In particular, the program's outcome depends upon the coordination of multiple groups and necessitates the voluntary participation of retailers and manufacturers. As shown in figure 1, consumers can begin applying for converter box coupons starting January 1, 2008, with NTIA requiring full distribution of coupons to begin no later than April 1, 2008. Consequently, some consumers that request coupons in January might have to wait months to receive their coupons. Complicating matters is uncertainty regarding retailer participation and readiness and potential challenges related to inventory planning. With limited or delayed retailer participation, consumers might face difficulties in redeeming their coupons for eligible converter boxes during the designated time period.

To help facilitate the DTV transition through comprehensive planning and risk management, we are recommending that the Chairman, FCC, in conjunction with public and private stakeholders, develop and communicate a comprehensive plan, including the attendant mitigation of risk, for the various aspects of the DTV transition, encompassing technical, policy, consumer outreach, and other critical elements.

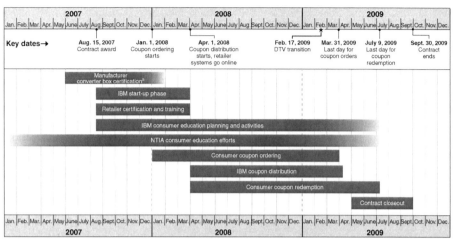

Source: GAO analysis of NTIA data.
aManufacturer converter box certification has no specified end date.

Figure 1. Time Line of Converter Box Subsidy Program.

We provided a draft of this report to FCC and the Department of Commerce (which contains NTIA) for comment. FCC did not directly indicate whether they agreed or disagreed with our recommendation. The Chairman of the FCC provided us with oral comments indicating he appreciated the role that we played in reviewing government programs. The Chairman also provided us with a draft document that he said represented the commission's actions over a number of years to meet the DTV transition. Regarding our recommendation, the Chairman said FCC does not have a formal plan in place that is publicly available, but that the various orders contained in FCC dockets amount to a plan. The Chairman also said that FCC staff working on the DTV transition do not believe our report gives them adequate credit for all the tasks they have accomplished related to the transition, which was the reason the Chairman indicated he provided us with the draft document. Similar to the elements we recommended FCC develop in a comprehensive plan, this draft document compiles FCC actions and other activities related to the transition and includes four main sections—technical goals, policy goals, consumer outreach goals, and other critical elements. This document appears to be the first step toward developing and communicating a comprehensive plan for various aspects of the transition, per our recommendation. The draft document describes a variety of actions related to DTV. However, the document neither meets the requirements for a strategic plan, nor is it sufficiently transparent to guide stakeholders to meeting the DTV goals or in serving as a road map to facilitate effective collaboration between the various stakeholders to ensure the intent of the DTV transition. Because the draft document does not directly address our recommendation, is relatively long (96 single-spaced pages), and includes FCC's actions related to technical matters not discussed in this report but which we will discuss in a subsequent report, we have chosen to characterize the document rather than include it in its entirety. We did not make any changes to our report based on the draft document we received from FCC. However, since interested parties might find the information provided by FCC useful, we are providing a Web link to the draft document, which is located at FCC draft document (or at http://www.gao.gov/fccdraft.pdf). Upon learning that we would not include the draft document in this report, the FCC Chairman submitted a letter, which we do include (see app. III), stating that generally accepted government auditing standards (GAGAS) requires us to publish FCC's draft document. The Chairman also stated that he had significant reservations and concerns with the report's approach and conclusions. However, he did not indicate whether he agreed or disagreed with our recommendation. We note that GAGAS does not require us to print in its entirety responses submitted by an agency in connection with our reports and allows us to characterize responses where suitable and to include or not include them as appropriate. Also, we are unable to evaluate the Chairman's statement that he had reservations and concerns about our approach and conclusions, as neither his letter nor the draft document indicate the basis for his reservations and concerns. FCC's response is reprinted in appendix III. In commenting on the draft of this report, the Department of Commerce (DOC) acknowledged the risks associated with the voluntary nature of industry participation in the converter box subsidy program and consumer outreach campaign, but stated that the solution is not the establishment of a digital transition czar or a single, government-mandated message. We did not recommend establishing a digital transition czar or a single, government-mandated message. DOC did not comment on our recommendation. Written comments from DOC are reprinted in appendix IV.

BACKGROUND

The United States is currently undergoing a transition from analog to digital broadcast television, often referred to as the DTV transition. The transition will enable the government to reallocate valuable spectrum from analog broadcast to public safety and other purposes. Digital transmission of television signals provides several advantages compared with analog transmission, such as enabling better quality picture and sound reception, as well as using the radiofrequency spectrum more efficiently than analog transmission. With traditional analog technology, pictures and sounds are converted into "waveform" electrical signals for transmission through the radiofrequency spectrum, while digital technology converts these pictures and sounds into a stream of digits consisting of zeros and ones for transmission.

The Digital Television Transition and Public Safety Act addresses the responsibilities of two federal agencies—FCC and NTIA—related to the DTV transition. The act directs FCC to require full-power television stations to cease analog broadcasting after February 17, 2009. The DTV transition also involves preparation on the part of American households. This preparation will require citizens' understanding of the transition and the actions that some might have to take to maintain television service. The specific equipment needs for each household to transition to DTV—that is, to be able to view broadcast digital signals—depends on certain key factors. As shown in figure 2, the method through which a household watches television, and whether it has already upgraded its television equipment to be compatible with digital television, will factor into the equipment needs of the household. While many households may need to take specific actions to ensure that they continue to receive television signals, others may not need to take any action. As we have previously reported, households with analog televisions that rely solely on over-the-air television signals received through a rooftop antenna or indoor antenna must take action to be able to view digital broadcast signals after the termination of analog broadcasting. Options available to these households include (1) purchasing a digital television set that includes a tuner capable of receiving, processing, and displaying a digital signal; (2) purchasing a digital-to-analog converter box, which converts the digital broadcast signals to analog so they can be viewed on an existing analog set; or (3) subscribing to a cable, satellite, or other service that provides the necessary signal to eliminate the need to acquire a digital-to-analog converter box.

TV type	Signal source	Equipment needed
Analog	Over-the-air	Digital-to-analog converter box
Analog	Cable or satellite	Provider will address
Digital	Over-the-air	Nothing
Digital	Cable or satellite	Provider will address

Source: GAO analysis of NTIA data.

Figure 2. Options for Viewing Digital Signals after the DTV Transition.

Recent surveys conducted by industry trade associations indicate that consumer awareness of the digital transition is low. The Association for Public Television Stations reported in September 2007 that 51 percent of participants surveyed were unaware that the transition was taking place. Another study conducted by the National Association of Broadcasters focused on households that primarily receive their television signals over-the-air—and will, therefore, be most affected by the transition—and reported that 57 percent of those surveyed were not aware of the transition. We are also in the process of conducting our own survey gauging, among other things, consumer awareness of the transition. We will discuss the results of our survey in a subsequent report.

To help inform consumers about the transition, in February 2007, eight private sector stakeholders launched the Digital Television Transition Coalition. These eight stakeholders are the Association for Maximum Service Television, Association of Public Television Stations, Consumer Electronics Association, Consumer Electronic Retailers Coalition, Leadership Conference on Civil Rights, LG Electronics, National

Sources: DTV Transition Coalition, CEA, FCC, NTIA, and RadioShack. These materials represent printed and online sources.

Figure 3. Examples of Consumer Outreach Materials about the DTV Transition.

Association of Broadcasters, and the National Cable and Telecommunications Association. These founding organizations comprise the coalition's steering committee and make decisions on behalf of the coalition. To better represent the interests of at-risk or underserved populations—such as the elderly—AARP later joined the steering committee. The coalition's mission is to ensure that no consumer is left without broadcast television due to a lack of information about the transition. Currently, the coalition has over 160 member organizations comprised of business, trade, and industry groups, as well as grassroots and membership organizations, and FCC.[6] See figure 3 for examples of consumer outreach materials.

The Digital Television Transition and Public Safety Act directed NTIA to establish a $1.5 billion subsidy program through which households can obtain coupons for the purchase of digital-to-analog converter boxes. In March 2007, NTIA issued a final rule that adopted regulations to implement the converter box subsidy program and, in August 2007, selected IBM to provide certain services for the program. NTIA, in accordance with the act, established that beginning January 1, 2008, households can request up to two $40 coupons toward the purchase of eligible[7] digital-to-analog converter boxes. Households requesting coupons must submit the name of the person requesting the coupon and a valid United States Postal Service address. A post office box will not be considered a valid address except in the cases of residents of American Indian reservations, Alaskan native villages, and other rural areas without home postal delivery.[8] Initially, any household is eligible to request and receive the coupons, but once $890 million worth of coupons have been redeemed, and issued but not expired, NTIA must certify to Congress that the program's initial allocation of funds is insufficient to fulfill coupon requests. NTIA will then receive $510 million in additional program funds, but any households requesting coupons during this second phase must certify that they do not receive cable, satellite, or other pay television service.[9] As shown in table 1, total possible program funding, which includes coupons redeemed, and issued but not expired, is $1.5 billion.

Table 1. Converter Box Subsidy Program Funding

Dollars in millions			
	Funds available for coupons	Funds available for administrative costs	Total
Initial allocation	$890	$100	**$990**
Additional allocation	$450	$60	**$510**
Grand total	**$1,340**	**$160**	**$1,500**

Source: GAO analysis of NTIA data.

The last day for consumers to request coupons is March 31, 2009, and coupons can be redeemed through July 9, 2009. As required by law, all coupons expire 90 days after issuance. The fully funded program could provide 33.5 million coupons.[10] After participants apply for a coupon, IBM will send the coupons to their address via United States Postal Service delivery. Consumers can redeem their coupons at participating retailers (both "brick and mortar" and online) for eligible converter boxes. Consumers can neither combine two $40 coupons for the purchase of one converter box, nor can they return converter boxes for a cash refund of the coupon amount, or exchange the converter box for another product, except another coupon-eligible converter box. In order to participate in the program, retailers must apply and meet certain standards, such as being a consumer electronics retailer for at least 1 year and having systems and procedures that can be easily audited. NTIA and IBM are responsible for certifying retailers. NTIA also established technical standards that included permitted, required, and disqualifying features that converter boxes must comply with in order to be coupon eligible. Manufacturers wishing to certify their converter boxes as coupon eligible must submit a notice of intent to NTIA 3 months prior to submitting their test results and sample models of their converter boxes. Then, manufacturers must submit test results demonstrating that the converter boxes meet the performance specifications and features established by NTIA, as well as two sample models of the converter box. NTIA will review the test results and sample models and will approve or disapprove of a converter box based on consultations with FCC.[11]

FEDERAL ENTITIES AND OTHER STAKEHOLDERS ARE FACILITATING THE TRANSITION, BUT COMPREHENSIVE PLANNING AND RISK MANAGEMENT IS LIMITED

FCC and NTIA have taken numerous steps intended to facilitate the transition. Likewise, the private sector has begun efforts related to advancing the transition. However, despite these public and private sector efforts, we found that no comprehensive plan or strategy exists with which to track transition efforts and measure progress. Such planning includes managing and mitigating risks, which we have previously reported as assisting organizations involved in other high stakes efforts similar to the DTV transition.

FCC and NTIA Have Taken Steps to Facilitate the Transition

FCC has primary responsibility under the Communications Act of 1934, as amended, to regulate the television broadcast industry. As such, FCC is required to periodically review the progress of the nation's transition to digital television, as well as to generally encourage the use of television in the public interest. The Digital Television Transition and Public Safety Act defines the specific responsibilities of FCC and other government agencies in the transition but does not specifically include overall responsibility to ensure the success of transition efforts. The act directs FCC to start auctioning the licenses for spectrum recovered in the digital transition no later than January 28, 2008, and to deposit auction proceeds in the U.S. Treasury by June 30, 2008.

FCC has taken steps to facilitate the DTV transition. FCC proposed and set deadlines and other requirements for broadcast stations upgrading their equipment to send digital signals. In addition, FCC conducts periodic reviews to report on progress in the DTV transition, including analyzing and proposing procedures and rule changes necessary to complete the transition. The most recent review released in May 2007 included a number of proposals and requests for comments from stakeholders. For example, the review proposed construction deadlines for preparing for the transition, as well as requested comments on what FCC can do to facilitate broadcasters' meeting the DTV transition deadline and whether coordination is needed between broadcasters and cable/satellite companies to ensure a smooth transition. FCC also worked to coordinate with outside stakeholders on the transition, such as holding a September 2007 workshop to provide an opportunity for interested parties to jointly discuss transition challenges and related issues. Additionally, FCC mandated the inclusion of digital tuners[12] in television receivers. Originally issued in 2002, FCC revised this mandate in 2005 to require that all televisions imported into the United States or shipped in interstate commerce after March 1, 2007, include a digital tuner. As we have previously reported, this action will help increase the number of households with the equipment to receive over-the-air digital signals.[13] FCC has proposed further steps to facilitate the transition. For example, in its recent review of the DTV transition, FCC proposed requiring all full-power television stations to file a form, detailing the station's current transition status, additional steps necessary in order to be prepared for digital-only operations after the transition, and a time line to accomplish those steps. If adopted, this would provide a comprehensive, national snapshot of stations' efforts to prepare for the transition.

FCC has also taken a number of actions focused on the technical aspects of the transition, such as determining channel assignments for broadcast stations following the transition, and tracking stations' readiness to broadcast digitally. We are conducting related work on the technical aspects and challenges of the transition and will issue a separate report on this work in 2008.

The Digital Television Transition and Public Safety Act also assigned responsibility to NTIA for the related converter box subsidy program. NTIA has taken steps to implement the subsidy program, such as issuing a contract to IBM to implement the program. We discuss the other steps NTIA has taken to implement the subsidy program later in this report.

Industry Stakeholders Have Also Begun Preparing for the DTV Transition

Industry stakeholders, including broadcasters, manufacturers, and retailers have begun efforts to prepare for the transition. For example, the broadcasters have been overhauling and replacing their transmission facilities, such as transmission lines, antennas, and digital transmitters and encoders to enable them to broadcast digitally.[14] Depending on each broadcaster's situation, the transition might require new towers or upgrades to existing towers. Most television stations (approximately 90 percent) throughout the country are now providing a digital broadcast signal in addition to their analog signal. In other efforts, manufacturers have designed, and retailers carry, a wide array of televisions that can receive digital signals. The Consumer Electronics Association estimated that for 2007 estimated wholesale revenues for digital televisions would be $26 billion. Manufacturers have also designed digital-to-analog converter boxes in order for analog televisions to receive and display digital signals. Manufacturers, broadcasters, and other private sector stakeholders are also assisting with consumer outreach efforts for the transition, which we will describe further later in this report.

Comprehensive Federal Planning and Risk Management for the Transition Is Limited

Despite efforts by the public and private sectors and ongoing coordination, we found that no comprehensive plan for the transition exists. FCC has included the DTV transition in its strategic plan for 2006 through 2011, as well as related annual performance reports. However, this particular plan is a high-level, agencywide plan, and FCC did not intend it to serve as a comprehensive plan or strategy for the overall transition. FCC officials were aware of planning information located in both its own and other organizations' documents. However, this information had not been coordinated in a comprehensive manner and was not accessible through any centralized planning document, rather it was scattered in parts of other documents across different organizations. We have previously reported on the benefits of having a comprehensive, centralized plan to facilitate program management and accountability.

Among other things, a comprehensive plan or strategy can detail milestones and key goals, which provide meaningful guidance for planning and measuring progress. Such plans can also establish deadlines for achieving objectives and assigning responsibility for program implementation. In recent months, there has been disagreement over federal agencies' roles and responsibilities for the transition. For example, officials at NTIA and FCC have different views on responsibilities related to the transition. In addition, FCC commissioners have expressed varying views to a congressional committee on the adequacy of the commission's activities and related responsibilities for the transition. We have previously reported on the importance of collaboration for issues cutting across more than one agency and in addressing complicated challenges like the DTV transition. Specifically, we identified agreeing on roles and responsibilities as a key practice of collaboration. We found no comprehensive plans for the overall transition that included these elements.

One aspect of comprehensive planning absent from transition efforts is assessing, managing, and mitigating risks. Several organizations we interviewed described potential risks to the transition. For example, one public broadcaster association said that one risk or "red flag" for transition efforts is whether various forms of media provide consumers with consistent and accurate information on the transition. Potential misinformation could create confusion among citizens, as well as in those organizations involved in the transition. Other risks cited included failing to reach certain consumers and existing funding proving inadequate for transition needs. Yet we found no examples of a formal risk assessment documenting these or other concerns, as well as potential solutions to mitigate them. FCC has risk assessment tools that it uses for internal activities. Assessing risks is also an element of FCC's annual performance report, and FCC told us it could explore applying risk assessment tools to ongoing transition efforts. NTIA has included risk management tools relevant to the transition, although this is only for its management of the converter box subsidy program. For example, NTIA required IBM to submit a risk management plan with its contract proposal, indicating how risks will be continually identified, documented, assessed, and communicated to project stakeholders and the criteria for risk management planning.

According to NTIA, it requires IBM to identify and assess risks associated with their ability to meet program objectives and to develop risk mitigation plans for high probability or high impact risks. NTIA said these risks are reviewed with IBM on a monthly basis In addition, NTIA said it has established an internal risk management process to identify and assess other program risks and to develop risk mitigation plans for those risks considered to be high probability or high impact.

Managing risks can help target limited resources and ensure critical dates are met, an important benefit given the transition's 2009 deadline. We have previously described the purpose of risk management as identifying potential problems before they occur to mitigate adverse impacts. Figure 4 depicts a risk management cycle representing a series of analytical and managerial steps, which are sequential, that can be used to assess risk, assess alternatives for reducing risks, choose among those alternatives, implement the alternatives, monitor their implementation, and continually use new information to adjust and revise the assessments and actions, as needed. The approach is dynamic and can be applied at various organizational levels. A viable risk management approach can also affect outcomes beyond the public sector in achieving national goals, which also has applicability to the DTV transition and the involvement of public and private stakeholders.

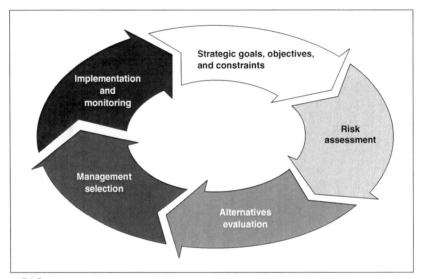

Source: GAO.

Figure 4. Risk Management Framework.

We have previously reported on the benefits of risk management in other high stakes efforts with similarities to the DTV transition. For example, like the DTV transition, Y2K involved a deadline when certain technology—computer systems—would face potential operational problems. In preparing the nation's computer systems for Y2K,[15] we provided a guide that included risk assessments, oversight, and the common thread of accountability at all levels.[16] We credited one federal agency's success in weathering Y2K, in part, due to reducing risks to facilities, systems, programs, and services during the critical rollover. Further, we have recently reported on the benefits of risk management in relation to the 2010 census, specifically in managing and overseeing contracts that are key to conducting a successful census.[17] Like the DTV transition, private organizations are involved in carrying out important public goals, in this case, the next census. Finally, we have reported on the advantages of managing risks for homeland security programs, namely to target federal funding for homeland security to maximize results and mitigate risks within available resource levels.[18] Effectively targeting resources is important to the DTV transition since funding appears limited.

PROGRESS IN CONSUMER EDUCATION ON THE DTV TRANSITION HAS BEEN MADE, BUT WIDESPREAD IMPLEMENTATION IS NOT YET UNDER WAY

Federal and private stakeholders are making progress in educating consumers about the DTV transition, with both independent and coordinated efforts under way. Some private sector stakeholders are taking the lead on outreach efforts on a voluntary basis. Overall, at the time of our report, many consumer education efforts were still in the planning stages and had not been widely implemented. Industry, government, and academic experts participating in our expert panel identified potential challenges and key components in launching a consumer education campaign.

Federal Stakeholders Have Begun Consumer Education Efforts

FCC and NTIA are both involved in consumer education about the DTV transition. For example, FCC has launched a Web site (DTV.gov) which, among other things, provides background information on the DTV transition and answers common consumer questions. In addition, FCC has met with some industry groups, consumer groups, and other government agencies and participated in public events intended to educate audiences about the transition. FCC also joined the DTV Transition Coalition, whose goal is to provide consumers with information about the transition. Moreover, in April 2007, FCC adopted a rule requiring all sellers of television-receiving equipment that does not include a digital tuner to prominently display a consumer alert that such devices will require a converter box to receive over-the-air broadcast television after February 17, 2009 (see fig. 5).

To ensure that retailers are in compliance, FCC staff have inspected over 1,000 retail stores and Web sites and issued over 250 citations with potential fines exceeding $3 million. In addition, FCC has issued notices to television manufacturers with potential fines over $2.5 million for importing televisions without digital tuners. In June 2007, FCC announced that it had rechartered an intergovernmental advisory committee comprising 15 representatives from local, state, and tribal governments to help it address, among other things, consumer education about the DTV transition. Similarly, it rechartered a consumer advisory committee that will also make recommendations to

FCC about the transition on behalf of consumers, with specific representation for people with disabilities and other underserved or at-risk populations. Finally, in August 2007, in response to a letter containing proposals on advancing consumer education submitted by members of Congress,[19] FCC released a notice of proposed rulemaking soliciting public comments on the proposals listed in the letter. These proposals include requiring television broadcasters to conduct on-air consumer education efforts and regularly report on the status of these efforts, requiring cable and satellite providers to insert periodic notices in customers' bills about the transition and their future viewing options, and requiring manufacturers to include information on the transition with any television set or related device they import or distribute in the United States. Each of the requirements mentions civil penalties for noncompliance. Another proposal on which FCC sought comment would have FCC work with NTIA to require that retailers participating in the converter box subsidy program detail their employee training and consumer information plans, as well as having FCC staff spot check the retailers for compliance. Also, FCC sought comments on a proposal requiring partners identified on FCC's DTV.gov Web site to report their specific consumer outreach efforts. The comment period on the notice of proposed rulemaking closed on September 17, 2007; the period to file any rebuttal closed October 1, 2007.

Source: FCC.

Figure 5. Consumer Advisory Alerts for Analog Televisions.

NTIA has also taken initial steps toward educating consumers about the transition. NTIA has statutory responsibility for the converter box subsidy program, for which Congress appropriated up to $5 million for education efforts. According to NTIA, its education efforts are focused on the subsidy program and within that on five groups most likely to lose all television service as a result of the transition: (1) senior citizens, (2) the economically disadvantaged, (3) rural residents, (4) people with disabilities, and (5) minorities. NTIA has begun outreach to these groups through partnerships with private organizations, as well as other federal agencies. In addition, it has created "information sheets" for consumers, retailers, and manufacturers that outline the subsidy program and are available on its Web site. NTIA said it has provided informational brochures in English and Spanish to the public and provided a copy to every member of Congress and federal agencies that serve some of the populations noted above. The agency also created a consumer hotline[20] that provides information about the transition in English and Spanish, as well as TTY numbers that provide information in English[21] and Spanish[22] to the hearing impaired. In addition, in August 2007, NTIA contracted with IBM to implement a broad consumer education component about the program, and a draft of this consumer education plan was submitted to NTIA on September 15, 2007.

While public sector entities are planning and, in some cases, launching consumer education efforts, widespread and comprehensive efforts have yet to be implemented. FCC officials told us that its efforts to educate consumers about the transition are limited, in large part because it does not currently have specific funds directed at consumer education. In a July 2007 testimony to Congress, the FCC Chairman stated that the agency is "working, consistent with its statutory authority and budgetary capacity to ensure that no American is left behind in this part of the digital revolution." In FCC's fiscal year 2008 budget request, it has requested $1.5 million for digital television consumer outreach specifically. FCC's outreach initiative would primarily use the media, Internet, publications, and participation in forums, public events, and community education programs to disseminate information. In addition, to maximize DTV outreach effectiveness and efficiency, it intends to coordinate programs with NTIA and other government agencies with DTV transition involvement. NTIA also has not fully implemented education efforts about its subsidy program in large part because it is contracting out the consumer education component of its program and, as mentioned previously, the contract was only recently awarded, and plans were in the development stage at the time of our review.

Private Sector Stakeholders Are Taking the Lead on Consumer Education Efforts, but Actions Are Voluntary and Widespread Implementation Is Limited

On a voluntary basis, some private sector stakeholders have begun planning and, in some cases, implementing measures to inform consumers about the DTV transition. One such private sector led effort is the DTV Transition Coalition, which encompasses over 160 organizations. According to the coalition, it has developed and consumer tested various messages about the transition, using surveys and focus groups of the affected consumers—the general population, senior citizens, minority groups, and over-the-air analog television households—to understand what messages are most effective in informing them about the transition. Subsequently, the coalition said it agreed upon one concise message that includes information about the transition itself, the rationale for the transition, and the ways consumers can effectively switch to DTV. In particular, the coalition suggests consumers can prepare for the transition by purchasing a DTV converter box, purchasing a new television set with a built in digital tuner, or subscribing to a pay television service such as cable, satellite, or telephone company video service provider. The coalition said its member organizations will distribute this information to their constituents, including senior citizens, the disabled, and minority groups. The coalition message will also be delivered to media outlets.

In addition to coordinated efforts within the coalition, private sector stakeholders also have independent education efforts under way. For example, a number of industry associations host Web sites that inform consumers of, among other things, common consumer questions about the transition, how to check if the television they own is digital-ready, and how to dispose of analog television sets. The Consumer Electronics Association (CEA) has launched a number of Web sites, one of which provides online education for retailers and their sales associates. Another CEA Web site informs consumers how to connect their television equipment, and CEA officials told us it will include guidance on how to connect a converter box to a television. One national retailer told us that it added a feature to its registers so that when a consumer purchases an analog television, a message about the DTV transition is printed on the bottom of the receipt. The National Cable and Telecommunications Association has created public service announcements about the transition in both Spanish and English, which are being aired by cable operators and networks in markets throughout the country. The National Association of Broadcasters also has plans to launch a public service announcement campaign related to the transition by the end of 2007, which will air on its local television broadcasting affiliates, independent stations, and broadcast networks.

Despite ongoing education efforts, since these actions are voluntary, the government cannot be assured of the extent of private sector efforts. For example, in a 2004 review, FCC deferred requiring retailers to label analog-only television equipment with information about the transition, leaving retailers and manufacturers to educate consumers voluntarily. Later, FCC determined that retailer and manufacturer efforts did not adequately inform consumers how analog-only television equipment would be affected by the transition and in 2007 implemented a labeling requirement. Moreover, given the different interests represented by industry stakeholders, messages directed at consumers vary and might lead to confusion. For example, in addition to providing information about why the transition is occurring, industry stakeholders also have incentives to provide consumers with information on a wide host of technology equipment or services that consumers could purchase, at varying costs. Advocates for the elderly, disabled, and non-English speaking households told us that they are concerned that their members will become confused by the options and end up purchasing equipment they do not need or more expensive equipment than necessary to maintain their television viewing.

Similar to progress made by public sector entities, widespread and comprehensive efforts have yet to be implemented by the private sector. Representatives from private sector organizations have told us there are several reasons why they are waiting to fully launch their consumer education campaigns. For example, they do not want to start too early and possibly lose the attention of consumers later on. Another reason is that they are awaiting key events to be finalized, such as when converter boxes will be available for purchase, so that education efforts can be complete. A number of nonprofit organizations told us that a lack of dedicated funding hampers their ability to educate and provide outreach to their constituents.

Expert Panelists Identified Potential Challenges and Key Components in Launching a Consumer Education Campaign

We convened an expert panel to discuss consumer education issues applicable to the DTV transition. These issues included potential challenges that may obstruct efforts and the key planning components of a consumer education campaign that will help to overcome some of those challenges. Expert panel members, as well as other private and public sector officials highlighted several challenges, as follows:

Prioritizing limited resources. With limited time and financial resources, it is likely to be a challenge for stakeholders to determine how best to allocate those resources within the campaign—for example, whether to target a smaller audience over a set period of time, versus targeting a broader audience over a shorter period of time. One expert noted, "There is a necessity of focus when you have limited resources. Rather than try to do too much and dilute your campaign, tighten it in and take your best shot."

Educating consumers who do not necessarily need to take action. Many of the outreach efforts will be focused on educating consumers on what to do to keep their television sets from going dark after the termination of analog broadcasts. However, a large proportion of U.S. households will not need to do anything—for example, because they have cable or satellite television service that will enable their analog set to continue to display programming. Because many messages focus on the actions that households that rely on over-the-air analog broadcasting need to take, consumers unaffected by the transition may become confused and purchase equipment they do not need. In our past work looking at a similar digital transition in Germany, we have described this potential confusion to cable and satellite households as a challenge of educating consumers about the transition.[23]

Reaching underserved populations. Conveying the message to underserved populations—for example, senior citizens, disabled, those residing in rural areas, or non-English speaking households will provide an added challenge. For example, many groups outreaching to consumers about the transition are doing so on Web sites, which may not be available to people who lack Internet access or are less technically savvy. Another challenge is providing information in a wide variety of formats, such as in different languages for non-English speaking consumers and in text, video, voice, and Braille for the disabled. Overall, a challenge of consumer education is that those households in need of taking action may be the least likely to be aware of the transition.

Furthermore, representatives from organizations representing underserved groups that we contacted relayed consumer education challenges that their members could face. A broad concern is that television sets will go dark on the transition date without adequate education about the transition and, for people in these groups, their televisions may be their sole source for receiving emergency and other local information. However, we heard these populations may be hard to locate and, therefore, expensive to reach. While representatives from a number of these organizations noted that they are in the best position to provide outreach to these groups, they also noted that they do not have the budget to target them comprehensively. AARP representatives expressed concern that retailers will downplay the various options—such as cable and satellite service and converter boxes—and try to convince consumers to purchase digital televisions. According to representatives from AARP and the Association for Public Television Stations, Americans over the age of 65 are more likely to receive their television programming through over-the-air analog broadcasting than those under 65. Regarding consumer education related to the converter box subsidy program, representatives from multiple organizations noted that education about the availability of coupons is especially important for underserved households for whom a television is an essential item, not a luxury item. Insofar as the subsidy will be administered on a first-come, first-served basis, there is a concern that these populations will be the last to hear about the program, putting them at a disadvantage for obtaining a coupon before the fund is depleted.

Aligning stakeholders. Panel members and other industry representatives also noted the challenge of aligning stakeholders—some who are natural competitors—to work together. In our past work, we have reported that federal agencies engaged in collaborative efforts—such as the DTV transition—need to create the means to monitor and evaluate their efforts to enable them to identify areas for improvement. Reporting on these activities can help key decision makers within the agencies, as well as clients and stakeholders, to obtain feedback for improving both policy and operational effectiveness.[24]

In addition to highlighting potential challenges, the expert panelists identified the key practices that are important to planning a consumer education campaign that will motivate consumers to take the steps needed to avoid television viewing disruptions, as well as help to alleviate identified challenges along the way (see table 2).

Table 2. Key Practices for Consumer Education Planning

Key practice	Description
Define goals and objectives	Define the goals of the communications campaign, e.g., to increase awareness or motivate a change in behavior. Define the objectives that will help the campaign meet those goals.
Analyze the situation	Analyze the situation, including any competing voices or messages, related market conditions, and key dates or timing constraints. Review relevant past experiences and examples to identify applicable "lessons learned" that may help to guide efforts.
Identify stakeholders	Identify and engage all the key stakeholders who will be involved in communications efforts. Clarify the roles and responsibilities of each stakeholder, including which entity or entities will lead overall efforts.
Identify resources	Identify available short- and long-term budgetary and other resources.
Research target audiences	Conduct audience research, such as dividing the audience into smaller groups of people who have relevant needs, preferences and characteristics, as well as measuring audience awareness, beliefs, competing behaviors, and motivators. Also, identify any potential audience-specific obstacles, such as access to information.
Develop consistent, clear messages	Determine what messages to develop based on budget, goals, and audience research findings. Develop clear and consistent audience messages; test and refine them.
Identify credible messenger(s)	Identify who will be delivering the messages and ensure that the source is credible with audiences.

Table 2. Continued

Key practice	Description
Design media mix	Plan the media mix to optimize earned media (such as news stories or opinion editorials) and paid media (such as broadcast, print, or Internet advertising). Identify through which methods (e.g., advertising in newsprint ads), how often (e.g., weekly or monthly) and over what duration (e.g., 1 year) messages will reach audiences.
Establish metrics to measure success	Establish both process and outcome metrics to measure success in achieving objectives of the outreach campaign. Process metrics assure the quality, quantity, and timeliness of the contractor's work. Outcome metrics evaluate how well the campaign influenced the attitudes and behaviors of the target audience(s) that it set out to influence.

Source: GAO analysis of expert panel discussion.

While still too early to evaluate the coalition's consumer education efforts, the coalition has employed strategies consistent with the key practices identified by the expert panel. For example, the coalition has identified stakeholders and conducted focus groups to test and refine its consumer messages. However, at the time of our report, it remains unclear whether public-private sector interaction can ensure a consistent message to prevent confusion or unnecessary purchases on the part of consumers. Moreover, the absence of comprehensive planning to assess and mitigate risks associated with the transition, including outreach efforts, may increase the potential for at-risk populations not adequately preparing for the transition.

NTIA HAS TAKEN STEPS TO IMPLEMENT A SUBSIDY PROGRAM FOR CONVERTER BOXES, BUT CHALLENGES REMAIN

NTIA has made progress in implementing the converter box subsidy program, including soliciting stakeholder comments and concerns, and selecting IBM in August 2007 to provide services for the program. However, the program faces challenges. In particular, the program's outcome depends on the coordination of several groups, and necessitates the voluntary participation of retailers and manufacturers. Moreover, uncertainty about retailers' participation, as well as readiness and potential challenges related to inventory planning, could hinder consumers' access to subsidy-eligible converter boxes.

NTIA Has Selected IBM to Implement the Converter Box Subsidy Program, but NTIA Remains Ultimately Responsible for the Program

NTIA completed several tasks related to the converter box subsidy program before it awarded the contract to IBM. In July 2006, NTIA issued a notice of proposed rulemaking inviting public comments on converter box manufacturing standards, the coupon application and redemption process, household eligibility, and ways of minimizing waste, fraud, and abuse. NTIA received 113 comments, including comments from manufacturers, retailers, media companies, advocacy groups, and professional services firms. As part of this process, NTIA also met with and received presentations from industry stakeholders. In addition, in July 2006, NTIA issued a request for information to conduct market research on the implementation of the converter box subsidy program. Specifically, NTIA asked vendors to comment on NTIA's proposed project objectives, time frames, corporate capability; proposed products, services, and solutions; and experience and cost estimates. NTIA released the final rule on the converter box subsidy program and issued a request for proposals for services related to the subsidy program in March 2007. A contract was awarded on schedule to IBM on August 15, 2007.

Although NTIA contracted with IBM to provide services for the converter box subsidy program, NTIA remains ultimately responsible for meeting the program's objectives. The contract is performance-based, which means that while NTIA requires IBM to meet certain outcomes and objectives, IBM is responsible for determining the specific means for doing so, including developing performance metrics.[25] NTIA remains responsible for ensuring that IBM meets the program objectives by determining that the performance metrics tie to the program objectives and by overseeing IBM's performance. The Office of Management and Budget's Office of Federal Procurement Policy identified managing the contractor's performance as the final step of its "Seven Steps to Performance-Based Acquisition," and this included adjusting staff roles and responsibility, assigning accountability for managing the contractor's performance, and regularly reviewing the contractor's performance in a working group. In addition, we have previously reported that agencies using performance-based contracting for complex, unique, and risky services need to maintain strong government involvement to mitigate risks.[26] We have found that effective contractor management and oversight includes having adequate resources and properly trained personnel, conducting ongoing surveillance throughout the performance period of the contract, and creating an official record of the contractor's performance.[27] To assist the agency in the implementation and oversight of the program, NTIA designated existing staff and is hiring new staff for contract management activities, and has required IBM to submit a quality assurance and surveillance plan for measuring its performance. Also, NTIA requested that IBM develop a Web-based electronic "dashboard" that provides real-time access to program status and performance measures, such as consumer coupon requests, retailer participation, and program financials. In addition, the National Oceanic and Atmospheric Administration (NOAA) is providing acquisition support to NTIA, which includes acting as the contracting officer, and temporarily locating NOAA acquisition staff in NTIA offices to provide acquisition expertise and assist NTIA personnel in managing the contract. IBM submitted a draft project management plan with its proposal. While IBM will determine the specifics of the consumer outreach plan and the technical solution for distributing and redeeming coupons, NTIA remains ultimately responsible for managing IBM's performance to ensure the program's successful completion.

Program Outcomes Depend on the Careful Coordination and Voluntary Participation of Several Groups, Some of Which May Face Challenges

The subsidy program's outcomes depend on the coordination and participation of NTIA, IBM, converter box manufacturers, retailers, and consumers. Figure 6 depicts the necessary, interrelated actions for the subsidy program. Manufacturers and retailers are voluntarily participating in the program, as NTIA does not have the authority to require their participation. According to NTIA, IBM has developed the technical solution for the program, which covers determining how consumers will request, receive, and redeem coupons, and how this will affect retailers' current point-of-sale systems.[28] In addition, manufacturers are creating converter boxes and submitting them to NTIA, which, in consultation with FCC, will review the results and determine whether the converter box meets the technical standards required of coupon-eligible converter boxes. In addition, IBM will certify eligible retailers where consumers can use their coupon for eligible converter boxes. NTIA and IBM will test IBM's solution for distributing and redeeming coupons. According to NTIA, one part of this testing will occur in December 2007, and includes processing a limited number of coupon requests, distributing a limited number of coupons to consumers, and having the coupons redeemed for eligible converter boxes by participating retailers.[29] NTIA and IBM will also be conducting consumer outreach specific to the program.

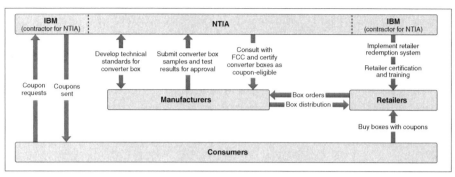

Source: GAO.

Figure 6. Coordination of Groups Involved in the Subsidy Program.

Retailers could face challenges that might limit or delay their participation in the subsidy program. At the time of our review, several retailers we contacted expressed concerns about the possibility of a redemption system that would affect their point-of-sale systems, noting that modifying these systems can be time-consuming, resource-intensive, and expensive, and can affect their other financial systems. Retailer representatives told us they will need more information about the contractor's technical solution and that March or April of 2008—3 to 4 months after consumers can begin requesting coupons—is a more likely time frame for retailers to be ready to participate in the program. In addition, retailers have pointed out that participating in the converter box subsidy program could require a considerable amount of effort for a one-time program with a product that has a limited shelf life[30] and low profit margin. The extent to which point-of-sale system modifications will be necessary and the potential impact on retailers will remain unknown until IBM presents its technical solution.

In addition, the unique nature of the converter box program and the limited time between the emergence and the depletion of demand for the converter boxes may present challenges for retailers and manufacturers in predicting demand and planning inventory accordingly. For example, retailer and manufacturer representatives noted that it is possible that demand could rapidly increase just before the transition and may then suddenly drop after February 17, 2009. This uncertain demand, as well as uncertainty about the extent of retailers' participation in the program, could affect the number of converter boxes that manufacturers produce and the corresponding availability of coupon-eligible converter boxes in stores. While a manufacturer and a consumer group we contacted expressed concern that retailers are not required to carry a certain level of inventory in their stores, a retailer trade association told us that requiring retailers to have a certain level of converter boxes in stock would be a large disincentive to participate in the program. However, manufacturers we contacted noted that their production of converter boxes would depend on receiving orders from retailers. These manufacturers could not tell us how many boxes they would produce or the expected retail cost of the boxes.

Challenges to Private Sector Participation Might Affect Consumers' Access to Converter Boxes

Uncertain retailer participation and converter box availability might affect consumers' access to converter boxes. Specifically, whether and when retailers participate may be affected by IBM's technical solution for accepting and redeeming coupons and the corresponding impact on retailers' point-of-sale systems. As previously noted, some retailer representatives have stated that they are more likely to be prepared to participate in the program in March or April 2008.

In accordance with the Digital Television Transition and Public Safety Act, consumers can begin applying for coupons starting January 1, 2008. In addition, NTIA requires full distribution of coupons to begin by April 1, 2008. Although IBM plans to distribute a limited number of coupons from January through March 31, 2008, unless they receive a coupon as part of the test solution, some consumers that request coupons in January may have to wait months to receive coupons. NTIA has stated that IBM will determine how to inform consumers requesting coupons in January 2008 when they will be able to redeem their coupons.

In addition, since retailers' participation in the subsidy program is voluntary, and currently uncertain, some manufacturer, advocacy, and retailer representatives we contacted expressed concern about consumers' ability to find participating retailers that are able to redeem coupons and have converter boxes in stock. Although the final rule does not require remedies if certain geographic areas lack participating retailers, NTIA requires IBM to measure retailers' participation by geographic area and intends to investigate areas with unusual participation patterns. In other words, if there is a large number of coupon requests from a small rural city, but no participating retailers in that area, NTIA may investigate the issue, but it does not have the authority to require retailers to participate. In addition, NTIA does not have the explicit authority to require that participating retailers maintain a certain level of inventory. Thus, it is uncertain whether consumers with coupons will be able to locate a participating retailer with converter boxes in stock. Some retailer and advocacy groups we contacted have pointed out that this could pose a challenge to certain groups, such as rural residents with limited access to retail outlets, or elderly and low-income populations for whom multiple trips to a store could be burdensome. Furthermore, some tribal groups have noted that tribal members living far from retailers will need to be able to purchase a coupon-eligible converter box online or direct from retailers and have it shipped to their homes. An advocacy group and a retailer we contacted noted that while online ordering could help address this issue, it might not be a viable option for some vulnerable groups. In addition, an online retailer told us they would need to assess the extent to which IBM's technical solution will affect their existing systems before deciding whether to participate.

CONCLUSION

The federal government has an interest in a smooth DTV transition since a primary goal of the transition is for the government to reclaim the spectrum that broadcasters currently use to provide analog television signals. The government is expected to be afforded billions of dollars in revenues from the spectrum auction. Moreover, the return of the spectrum will ease the spectrum scarcity facing public safety first responders and engender economic growth and consumer value from spectrum redeployed to wireless services. The approaching deadline for the DTV transition has heightened efforts among public and private organizations to ensure that the United States achieves a smooth transition to digital television by February 17, 2009. FCC, NTIA, and private sector organizations have begun important efforts toward this end, including policy and technical decisions and outreach to consumers on the options that they can take to maintain access to their television programming. These efforts are ongoing, and the involvement of multiple organizations in assisting with the transition is a positive demonstration of the commitment of public and private stakeholders to meet the 2009 deadline.

In an undertaking as complicated as the DTV transition, careful planning— including managing and mitigating risks—is needed to help organizations track and complete their transition efforts. Managing and mitigating risks is especially important as the transition's success will rely on participation by both the public and the private sectors, effective collaboration among these groups, targeting resources to reach citizens of various demographics across the country, and meeting critical dates to achieve results before the legislatively set deadline to turn off analog signals. Current public and private sector efforts might be adequate to ensure a smooth transition, free of consumer disruptions. However, not having a comprehensive plan for the DTV transition limits the government's ability to measure efforts against planned goals, set milestones, and assess risks. This raises uncertainty, including whether consumers, particularly underserved and otherwise vulnerable populations, will have the information necessary to respond to the transition and to maintain their access to television programming. Furthermore, a comprehensive plan could help identify gaps or other areas for improvement that further planning and risk management could address. Voluntary transition efforts combined with the absence of responsibility for facilitating the overall DTV transition means that accountability for a successful transition cannot be assured. Since FCC has the broadest telecommunications responsibilities in the federal government, it is in the best position to increase assurance of a successful transition through increased attention to high-level comprehensive planning, performance measurement, and risk mitigation efforts.

RECOMMENDATION FOR EXECUTIVE ACTION

To help facilitate the DTV transition through comprehensive planning and risk management, in consultation with public and private stakeholders, we recommend that the Chairman, FCC, develop and communicate a comprehensive plan for the various aspects of the DTV transition, encompassing technical, policy, consumer outreach, and other critical elements. The plan should include (1) detailed goals, milestones, and time frames that can be used to gauge performance and progress, identify gaps, and determine areas for improvement; (2) strategies for collaboration between public and private sector stakeholders to agree on roles and responsibilities; (3) a description of reporting requirements to track stakeholder efforts against planned goals; and (4) strategies for managing and mitigating risks to avoid potential problems and target federal resources.

APPENDIX I: OBJECTIVES, SCOPE, AND METHODOLOGY

The objectives of this report are to provide information on the progress of the digital television (DTV) transition and, in particular, the progress made (1) by federal entities, in conjunction with other stakeholders, in facilitating the transition; (2) in educating consumers about the transition and any related challenges; and (3) in implementing a subsidy program for converter boxes and any related challenges.

To meet these objectives, we reviewed statutes, regulations, and federal agency planning documents that broadly define the role of the Federal Communications Commission (FCC) and the National Telecommunications and Information Administration (NTIA) in the DTV transition. In addition, we reviewed strategic plans for both FCC and NTIA, FCC periodic reviews and orders related to the transition, and testimony statements of FCC, NTIA, and officials from broadcasting, retail, manufacturing, cable, and advocacy groups. Further, we spoke with a wide variety of stakeholders in the transition, including FCC and NTIA officials, as well as the nine steering committee members of the DTV Transition Coalition: AARP, Association for Maximum Service Television, Association of Public Television Stations, Consumer Electronics Association, Consumer Electronic Retailers Coalition, Leadership Conference on Civil Rights, LG Electronics, National Association of Broadcasters, and the National Cable and Telecommunications Association. We also interviewed five retailers, the North American Retail Dealers Association, two additional converter box manufacturers, the Satellite Broadcasting and Communications Association, a television station that has completed its transition to digital, four state broadcaster associations, and two additional special interest groups that act on behalf of underrepresented populations. We also attended two meetings of the DTV Transition Coalition.

Further, we convened a half-day panel of 14 senior management-level experts in strategic communications to identify and come to consensus on key planning components for consumer education and outreach. The panel succeeded in agreeing upon the key phases of a public education outreach campaign. Additionally, the panel discussed key components of the implementation and measurement phases of an outreach campaign. We selected these experts based on their experience overseeing a strategic communications or social marketing campaign or other relevant expertise. The experts represented private, public, and academic institutions: AARP, Academy for Educational Development, American Legacy Foundation, APCO Worldwide, Edelman, Fleishman-Hillard, GolinHarris, Issue Dynamics Inc., Ogilvy, PodTech (representing Sweden's DTV transition), Population Services International, Porter Novelli, Food and Nutrition

Service within the U.S. Department of Agriculture, and the Darden School of Business at the University of Virginia.

Finally, to learn about the subsidy program, we reviewed comments submitted to NTIA regarding the proposed program rules. We reviewed NTIA's Request for Proposal for administering the program, questions submitted to NTIA from prospective bidders, NTIA's answers to those questions, and the NTIA contract for the converter box subsidy program. However, NTIA awarded the contract in August 2007, which was at the end of our audit work. Thus, our review was preliminary, and adequate time has not yet passed for us to evaluate the contractor or NTIA's performance in administering the contract. We also interviewed the National Oceanic and Atmospheric Administration, the agency acting as NTIA's contracting officer for the program. To determine important practices in administering performance-based contracts, we reviewed the Office of Federal Procurement Policy's "Seven Steps to Performance-Based Services Acquisition," as well as prior GAO reports. We conducted our review from January 2007 to August 2007 in accordance with generally accepted government auditing standards.

APPENDIX II: KEY PLANNING COMPONENTS, IMPLEMENTATION CHALLENGES, AND EVALUATION ELEMENTS OF PUBLIC EDUCATION OUTREACH

The DTV transition presents a communications challenge that is relatively unique—inform the U.S. population, and particularly affected subgroups within that population, about an issue that will require some households to take action within a fixed period of time. Although the DTV transition is a communications challenge, the process for informing the public about this issue is similar to the course of action that occurs in many public education outreach campaigns, particularly those looking to affect a behavior change. These public education campaigns typically have three fundamental stages: planning, implementation, and evaluation. In order to determine the extent to which a campaign has reached its goals, the steps that comprise each stage must be understood.

We convened a panel of strategic communications and social marketing experts on June 28, 2007, to better understand the steps that comprise a consumer education campaign. The panel focused on communications campaigns that are intended to elicit a one-time action or behavior change. The objectives of the panel were to (1) achieve consensus on key practices of the planning stage of the campaign process; (2) understand what, if any, potential challenges might obstruct the implementation of consumer education efforts when moving from principles to practice; and (3) understand some of the key ways to evaluate the campaign on process and outcomes.

Key Practices for Planning an Effective Consumer Education Campaign

We asked the panelists to write their own list of the key elements of a consumer education campaign. Once they completed writing their list, each expert shared one of their items and the discussion continued around the table until all had given one key element. Panelists were then encouraged to share other elements on their list that had not yet been shared, or others they thought of during the discussion. At the end of the session, there were 40 discrete elements that had been suggested by panelists and then discussed.

The panel agreed to allow us to contact them at a later date to reach consensus on the key elements of the planning stage of a consumer education campaign. In the week after the panel concluded, we analyzed the 40 proposed elements and collapsed them into 11 broader categories. Each of the panelists was then sent an e-mail showing the 11 categories with their corresponding definitions, and a description of how each of the 40 items fit into the 11 broad categories. The panel was requested to provide feedback in the form of an agreement with the 11 categories created or to offer suggestions about how they would modify those categories. We received comments from 11 of the 14 panelists and the non-response from the other 3 was viewed as consensus with our analysis. Based on the panelists' feedback, we created a final list of 9 key practices for planning a consumer education campaign. As discussed previously in this report, these key practices (in no particular order) are (1) define goals and objectives, (2) analyze the situation, (3) identify stakeholders, (4) identify resources, (5) research target audiences, (6) develop consistent, clear messages, (7) identify credible messengers, (8) design media mix, and (9) establish metrics to measure success. While this list was created with the DTV campaign in mind (focusing on a one-time behavior change), the goal in creating this list was that it could be used to provide a framework for evaluating other consumer education outreach programs as well.

Key Implementation Challenges That Might Obstruct Consumer Education Efforts

In this panel session, participants were asked to draw upon their previous experiences with public education campaigns to identify key challenges they have faced when moving from the principles of the planning stage to the practices of the implementation stage. As discussed previously in this report, the following challenges were the four that stood out as the most pressing implementation challenges: (1) prioritizing limited resources, (2) educating consumers who do not necessarily need to take action, (3) reaching underserved populations, (4) aligning stakeholders.

Key Elements for Measuring Campaign Effectiveness

The final session of our expert panel was a discussion about the role of evaluation in a strategic communications campaign. While the evaluation phase is typically considered a distinct component, it can be integrated into all parts of a campaign. The evaluation process for a public education campaign is typically thought of in three phases: (1) inputs, which includes the investments of the evaluation, such as resources, staff, partners, and technology; (2) outputs, which monitors the performance of the contractor or service provider in conducting the program; and (3) outcomes, which evaluates the impact of a campaign at different time intervals. This process is often represented schematically by a logic model, which is an evaluation tool used to describe a program's components and desired results and explain the strategy—or logic—by which the program is expected to achieve its goals.[1]

Because the panelists were not evaluation experts, per se, but rather practitioners who used evaluation and measurement in their own campaigns, the focus of the discussion was primarily on the role of the outcomes measurement phase. There was also a brief discussion of outputs measurement. This discussion was not as in-depth as it may have been with a panel of evaluation experts. The practitioner perspective, however, yielded some valuable insight to the process.

The panelists agreed that evaluation is an essential element of any public education campaign. In fact, panelists believed that evaluation is a "must do" even with limited resources. Panelists suggested that, with limited resources, a government outreach campaign must work with stakeholders that also have a vested interest in the issue, in order to leverage both the work and funding. One panelist noted that, in the case of the DTV transition, there are "two giants with a vested interest—the media and the consumer electronics industry." The panelist suggested that the federal government coordinate its efforts with these and other interest groups to conduct most of the outcomes evaluation. Furthermore, panelists stressed the importance of having a clear understanding of the goals and objectives of the campaign when designing the metrics that comprise the evaluation component. Once the goals are clearly defined, planners can establish the necessary targets to measure the effectiveness of a campaign.

Panel Selection and Representation

In selecting the panelists, at the institutional level, we sought to represent a broad spectrum of relevant expertise, including people from private sector communications firms; special interest groups with relevant experience in reaching out to special needs populations; government agencies with relevant experience in communicating one-time messages or information requiring a behavior change; academic experts in marketing or social marketing; and relevant nonprofit organizations. At the individual level, selection of the panelists was based on the following criteria:

- relevant experience in comparable outreach campaigns, either based on experience in communicating comparable messages or experiences in communicating to comparable populations;
- Vice President or Senior Vice President level or above; if not applicable, individuals who have led relevant outreach campaigns;
- recognized as an expert by peers;
- recommended as an expert by peers;
- several years of experience in the professional/academic field; and
- based in or around Washington, D.C. (because we are unable to pay any costs for participation, including travel costs).

The following organizations were represented on the expert panel:

- *Strategic communications firms*: APCO Worldwide; Edelman Worldwide; Fleishman-Hillard; GolinHarris; Issue Dynamics, Inc.; Ogilvy; and Porter Novelli;
- *Academic institutions/nonprofits/associations*: AARP; Academy for Educational Development; American Legacy Foundation; Population Services International; University of Virginia, Darden School of Business; and
- *Government agencies*: Swedish Government; U.S. Department of Agriculture, Food and Nutrition Service.

REFERENCES

[1] The radiofrequency spectrum is the part of the natural spectrum of electromagnetic radiation lying below 300 gigahertz. It is the medium that makes possible wireless communications, including cellular and paging services, radio and television broadcasting, radar, and satellite-based services.

[2] The Congressional Budget Office estimated auction proceeds from the spectrum currently used by broadcasters has an expected value of $12.5 billion.

[3] These sets, which only have a National Television Systems Committee (NTSC) tuner, are only capable of receiving and displaying analog signals.

[4] Such a television would include an Advanced Television Systems Committee (ATSC) tuner.

[5] Pub. L. No. 109-171, title 3.

[6] While NTIA is not an official coalition member, the agency has been participating in coalition activities since its inception. The coalition, as well as FCC and NTIA, have created Web sites providing information on the DTV transition and converter box subsidy program. These Web sites are available for viewing at the following addresses: www.dtvtransition.org, www.dtv.gov, and www.ntia.doc.gov/dtvcoupon.

[7] NTIA established technical and performance specifications that converter boxes must meet to be eligible for the subsidy program.

[8] These residents may have to provide additional information to identify the physical location of the household.

[9] There is up to $510 million in additional funds, bringing total possible program funding to $1.5 billion, which includes up to $1.34 billion in coupon funds, and up to $160 million in administrative funds.

[10] Assuming the full administrative amounts are used for administrative expenses, with none of that amount going toward coupons.

[11] NTIA entered into a memorandum of understanding with FCC establishing that FCC will test converter box samples at NTIA's direction.

[12] Digital tuners decode the digital signal and turn it into the picture that appears on the television screen.

[13] GAO, *Telecommunications: Additional Federal Efforts Could Help Advance Digital Television Transition*, GAO-03-7 (Washington D.C.: Nov. 8, 2002).

[14] FCC has not yet adopted general rules mandating low-power television to transition to digital broadcasting by February 17, 2009, or how these stations will operate thereafter. There are also more than 2,300 licensed low-power television stations operating throughout the United States.

[15] Federal agencies faced the potential for critical computer system failures at the turn of the century due to incorrect information processing relating to dates. Possible disruptions of Y2K included delayed financial transactions, grounded flights, and lost power.

[16] GAO, *Y2K Computing Challenge: Day One Planning and Operations Guide* ,GAO/AIM D-10.1.22 (Washington, D.C.: October 1999).

[17] GAO, *2010 Census: Preparations for the 2010 Census Underway, but Continued Oversight and Risk Management Are Critical*, GAO-07-1106T (Washington D.C.: July 17, 2007).

[18] GAO, *Strategic Budgeting: Risk Management Principles Can Help DHS Allocate Resources To Highest Priorities*, GAO-05-824T (Washington D.C.: June 29, 2005).

[19] These suggestions were in the form of a letter sent to FCC and signed by various congressional representatives.

[20] 1-888-DTV-2009.

[21] 1-877-530-2634.

[22] 1-866-495-1161.

[23] GAO, *Telecommunications: German DTV Transition Differs from U.S. Transition in Many Respects, but Certain Key Challenges Are Similar*, GAO-04-926T (Washington D.C.: July 21, 2004).

[24] GAO, *Results-Oriented Government: Practices That Can Help Enhance and Sustain Collaboration among Federal Agencies*, GAO-06-15 (Washington, D.C.: Oct. 21, 2005).

[25] For performance-based contacts, the Federal Acquisition Regulation allows contactors to develop performance measures.

[26] GAO, *Contract Management: Guidance Needed for Using Performance-Based Service Contracting*, GAO-02-1049 (Washington D.C.: Sept. 23, 2002).

[27] GAO, *Defense Acquisitions: Tailored Approach Needed to Improve Service Acquisition Outcomes* ,GA O-07-20 (Washington D.C.: Nov. 9, 2006) and *Contract Management: Opportunities to Improve Surveillance on Department of Defense Service Contracts*, GAO - 05-274 (Washington D.C.: Mar. 17, 2005).

[28] Point-of-sale systems record purchases, payments, returns, and exchanges, as well as send the individual transactions to the company's internal inventory and accounting systems. They can also include an external component of 'in real time' communication with financial institutions, merchant banks, or other sources to identify the validity of the method of payment and authorize utilization of that method (credit card, debit card, gift card, check, etc).

[29] The entire testing period runs from August 16, 2007, to March 31, 2008. It is possible that the contractor could move out of the start-up phase before March 31, 2008. April 1, 2008, is the date by which the coupon operational period must begin; thus, March 31, 2008, is the latest possible end date for the testing period.

[30] Retailers we contacted noted that demand for the converter boxes would likely peak just before the transition and rapidly fall afterward.

Appendix II

[1] For additional information on how logic models are used in a public outreach campaign, see GAO, *Program Evaluation: Strategies for Assessing How Information Dissemination Contributes to Agency Goals,* GAO-02-923 (Washington D.C. Sept. 30, 2002).

In: Digital Television: On the Threshold
Editor: Mark L. Goldstein, pp. 73-76

ISBN: 978-1-60456-693-2
© 2008 Nova Science Publishers, Inc.

Chapter 4

DIGITAL TELEVISION TRANSITION: QUESTIONS ON THE DTV CONVERTER BOX SUBSIDY PROGRAM AND A DTV INTER-AGENCY TASK FORCE[*]

Government Accountability Office

November 19, 2007

The Honorable John D. Dingell
Chairman
Committee on Energy and Commerce
House of Representatives

Dear Chairman Dingell:

This letter responds to questions from your November 7, 2007, letter inquiring about issues discussed at the October 17, 2007, hearing before the Subcommittee on Telecommunications and the Internet on the digital television (DTV) transition.[1] In your letter, you asked if we have concerns about the converter box subsidy program. You also asked whether the National Telecommunications and Information Administration (NTIA) should prepare for a potential shortfall in program funding, in part by developing a process to address a potential shortfall. You also asked us to elaborate on the statutory provisions that we believe provide the Federal

---

[*] This chapter is an excerpted, indexed edition of GAO report GAO-08-297R, Dated November 19, 2007

Communications Commission (FCC) with the necessary authority to convene an inter-agency task force. We prepared our responses during November 2007 in accordance with generally accepted government auditing standards. Our responses are based on our previous and ongoing work and our knowledge of the subjects raised by your questions. Because our responses are based on work for which we sought and incorporated agency comments, we did not seek agency comments on our responses to these questions.

Regarding the converter box subsidy program, we believe the subsidy program faces challenges that could affect the outcome of the program. These challenges include the coordination of several groups, readiness of retailers to accept coupons, and potential issues related to inventory planning. In particular, the subsidy program's outcome depends on the coordination and participation of NTIA, its contractor IBM, converter box manufacturers, retailers, and consumers. Manufacturers and retailers are voluntarily participating in the program, as NTIA does not have the authority to require their participation. Further, retailers we contacted expressed concerns about the possibility of a coupon redemption system that would affect their point-of-sale systems, noting that modifying these systems can be time-consuming, resource-intensive, and expensive, and can affect their other financial systems. Retailers told us that March or April of 2008—3 to 4 months after consumers can begin requesting coupons—is a likely time frame for retailers to be ready to participate in the program. Retailers also told us that participating in the converter box subsidy program could require a considerable amount of effort for a one-time program with a product that has a limited shelf life and low profit margin. In addition, since retailers' participation in the subsidy program is voluntary, some manufacturer, advocacy, and retailer representatives we contacted expressed concern about consumers' ability to find participating retailers that are able to redeem coupons and have converter boxes in stock. Furthermore, uncertain demand for the converter boxes, as well as uncertainty about the extent of retailers' participation in the program, could affect the number of converter boxes that manufacturers produce and the corresponding availability of coupon-eligible converter boxes in stores. During our ongoing work associated with the DTV transition, we will continue to analyze and examine the converter box subsidy program, exploring issues such as fraud and retailer knowledge about the program.

We have not evaluated whether NTIA should prepare for a shortfall in funding for the converter box subsidy program. However, we note that the Digital Television Transition and Public Safety Act provided an initial amount of $990 million for the converter box subsidy program, of which $100 million can be used for administrative expenses. If NTIA determines the initial allocation of funds is insufficient to fulfill coupon requests, the act requires NTIA to certify that the funds are insufficient to the House Committee on Energy and Commerce and the Senate Committee on Commerce, Science, and Transportation. The act provides that 60 days following this notification, NTIA will receive $510 million in additional program funds, of which $60 million can be used for administrative expenses (see table 1). NTIA established that during the initial funding allocation, any household is eligible to request and receive coupons, but once NTIA receives the additional allocation of funds (after $890 million worth of coupons have been redeemed, and issued but not expired) any households requesting coupons during this second phase must certify that they do not receive cable, satellite, or other pay television service. In addition, NTIA required that IBM develop a Web-based electronic "dashboard" that provides real-time access to program status and performance measures, including the number of coupons pending, mailed, redeemed, expired, and canceled. NTIA officials told us that they will monitor the coupon metrics on the electronic dashboard and use this information to inform the congressional committees if they would need the additional funds. They added that this monitoring should help avoid any lapse in depletion of the initial $890 million and receiving the additional funding.

Table 1. Converter Box Subsidy Program Funding

Dollars in millions	Funds available for coupons	Funds available for administrative costs	Total
Initial allocation	$890	$100	**$990**
Additional allocation	$450	$60	**$510**
Grand total	**$1,340**	**$160**	**$1,500**

Source: GAO analysis of NTIA data.

In response to your question about the statutory authority for FCC to convene an interagency task force, the Federal Advisory Committee Act[2] (FACA) authorizes federal agencies (in addition to Congress and the President) to establish federal advisory committees, which may consist of private as well as public sector members. FCC has several federal advisory committees that provide advice and recommendations to the commission on numerous technical, operational, and consumer telecommunications issues. All of FCC's federal advisory committees are discretionary, meaning the committees were not required to be established by law but rather were established by FCC. FACA requires advisory committees to have membership fairly representing an array of viewpoints and interests. We reviewed FCC's federal advisory committees in 2004[3] and found that its advisory committees had members representing numerous sectors across telecommunications including industry, academia, advocacy groups, private consulting, and government. We note that in June 2007, FCC rechartered an intergovernmental advisory committee comprising 15 representatives from local, state, and tribal governments to help it address, among other things, consumer education about the DTV transition. Similarly, it rechartered a consumer advisory committee that will also make recommendations to

FCC about the DTV transition on behalf of consumers, with specific representation for people with disabilities and other underserved or at-risk populations.

If you or your staff have any questions or would like to discuss this response, please contact me at (202) 512-2834 or goldsteinm@gao.gov.

Sincerely yours,

Mark L. Goldstein
Director, Physical Infrastructure Issues

REFERENCES

[1] GAO, Digital Television Transition: Preliminary Information on Progress of the DTV Transition, GAO-08-191T. (Washington, D.C.: October 17, 2007).

[2] Pub. L. 92-463, codified at 5 U.S.C. app. 2.

[3] GAO, Federal Communications Commission: Federal Advisory Committees Follow Requirements, but FCC Should Improve Its Process for Appointing Committee Members , GAO-05-36. (Washington, D.C.: Dec. 10, 2004).

INDEX